MW00610927

Successfully Implementing Lean Six Sigma

Successfully Implementing Lean Six Sigma

The Lean Six Sigma Deployment Roadmap

Keith M. Gardner

PINNACLE PRESS

SALINE, MICHIGAN

Graphics and cover design by Brian Leach

ISBN: 978-0-9859435-0-9
Library of Congress Control Number: 2012948280

Published by
Pinnacle Press
6453 Hollowtree Court
Saline, MI 48176

Published 2013
Second printing 2014
Printed in the United States of America
19 18 17 16 15 14   10 9 8 7 6 5 4 3 2

Download a free, full-color, 24″ x 36″ or 11″ x 17″ PDF of the eMRI Lean Six Sigma Deployment Roadmap at www.e-mri.net/roadmap.htm.

For additional information on Lean Six Sigma training and consulting, visit www.e-MRI.net.

It is not enough to do your best;
you must know what to do,
and then do your best.

—W. Edwards Deming

CONTENTS

ACKNOWLEDGMENTS

It is impossible to list all the people who helped make this book possible, yet I will name a few of them.

To begin with, I am indebted to all the people at eMRI that I have had a chance to work with and learn from over the years. There are too many of you to list. I especially need to thank Mark Lindsay and Kristin Lynch for providing feedback as I went through the process of writing this book. I also thank Mark for having been an invaluable mentor to me over the past 15 years.

My editor, Bob Halstead, was a valued addition to the team. I appreciated not only his editing ability but his infinite patience.

I also need to thank the hundreds of client organizations and thousands of people that I have come in contact with over the years. I learned a tremendous amount from you and appreciate your letting me and my eMRI colleagues work with you. Without your involvement and engagement, this book would not have been possible.

I also recognize our academic partners, the University of North Florida and Midlands Technical College, for support in helping to create those client relationships. People such as John Leighty and Linda Stuart at Midlands and Bob Wood at North Florida have played a key role in eMRI's success.

Lastly, I give the biggest thanks to my wife Kathi, daughter Samantha, and son Marshall for putting up with the endless travel and long hours that I have inflicted on them over the past 15 years. Without their support, this book would still be a distant dream.

PREFACE

In my prior career as a business owner and executive, and now as Dean of Continuing Education at the University of North Florida, I have personally seen the positive impact that a well-structured Lean Six Sigma program can make on an organization. In my current role as dean and as a member of several business advisory boards, I interact with hundreds of business leaders every year to discuss business strategy and how the university can support their organizations. The things that Lean Six Sigma can provide, such as cost reductions and improvements in quality, are invariably high on their lists.

It is also clear from these interactions that not all organizations which initiate a Lean Six Sigma program are successful. My observation is that many of the programs that fail, do so because executives and managers don't understand what is required to be successful. Because of this, I strongly encourage readers to use Keith's insights in this book.

I have known Keith for over 10 years, and he has truly been both a visionary and a practical problem solver in implementing process-improvement programs throughout the United States and the world. He and his company, eMRI, have trained hundreds of companies in 25 countries around the world. He is the cofounder of the Center for Quality and Process Improvement at the University of North Florida, Jacksonville, Florida, and also at Midlands Technical College in Columbia, South Carolina. In addition, he serves on our Executive Dean's Council at the University of North Florida and is one of our Executives in Residence at the University of North Florida's Division of Continuing Education.

It is exciting to see one of the foremost thought leaders I have met share a comprehensive methodology and strategy for implementing programs. At the end of the day, this book will provide the reader with common-sense solutions to implementing Lean Six Sigma or, I would argue, any other problem-solving methodology in his or her organization. eMRI's seven-phase roadmap takes you through the implementation process, and will enlighten and aid in providing an approach to implement change and improve processes for all. The breadth of eMRI's experience is evident in the examples used to illustrate key points.

Robert L. Wood Jr., DLP
Dean, Division of Continuing Education
University of North Florida

FOREWORD

UnitedHealth Group has been one of the true success stories of the past 15 years, having grown from a company of less than $4 billion in 1995 to one approaching $95 billion in 2011, a growth rate of nearly 25 percent per year. In 1998, though, that future success was less than certain. UnitedHealth Group had just announced that it was taking a $900 million charge to earnings and was restructuring its business after a decade of mergers, acquisitions, and divestitures. At the core of restructuring was an administrative process-improvement program. I was charged with ensuring that these process improvements led to true value realization, and built the tools and organization to do that. We proceeded to reduce our operating structure by nearly $200 million in two years. More important, we aligned processes and capabilities across the enterprise, establishing the platform for our later growth. In those two years we installed very little new technology; instead we focused on operational improvements. In our after-action review, we pointed to three key success factors: dedicated and focused leadership, an emphasis on process improvement over technology investments, and the discipline of our value-realization process.

On the other hand, we had relied extensively on a consulting group to help us lead this program. While the consultant had been an excellent partner for us, we needed an internal process-improvement capability and culture to drive change ourselves. I was asked to lead this effort.

Within the first three years we developed and deployed our own version of Six Sigma, which we called Just Right Service, and trained over 3,500 executives and Lean Six Sigma Master Black Belts, Black Belts, and Green Belts. In the first full year of the program we initiated over 100 Black Belt projects and generated $10 million in total return. Today, the operating discipline that started with that program is still going strong within UnitedHealth Group. Most projects have a project charter, most employees know how to build a process map and read a SIPOC, and every project Champion knows what a value-realization plan is.

At the same time, we struggled with some of the things that every leader of change faces. First, there was often already a "known solution" for every problem we faced (often, expensive new technology). Second, and associated with the first problem, executives were eager to deploy a solution; our initial projects sometimes took longer to complete, as team members learned how to solve problems themselves instead of merely implementing the "known solution." This created a third problem associated with standard process-improvement approaches. In installing these tools, I sometimes became overzealous about the application of the tools, rather than the outcomes of the projects. The goals became how many people trained, how many projects were under way, whether we followed the process … and the outcomes of each project became secondary.

I took these lessons into my last role at United, leading what we called Quality and Affordability Programs. In that role I was responsible for taking all the tools that a health-care company like UnitedHealth Group has—its network and contracts, administrative and clinical programs, and research base and data—and organized them to more effectively reduce medical cost and improve clinical quality for the 45 million Americans we served. Once again, we used process design as our primary tool. We de-emphasized the tools of process improvement (although they were always in full use), and refocused on realizing financial value (turning improvement into real, tangible, measurable value). As a result, we were again very successful, realizing $900 million in financial benefits within two years.

But we again became dissatisfied with our results. We looked at the overall process of applying our "health plan tools" and realized that while highly effective tools, they were sometimes being delivered at the wrong part of the overall health-care system. For example, the intention of programs like "prior authorization" is to help doctors and patients use evidence-based research as part of their medical decision making, but they often become overly complex administrative processes that occur after a patient and a doctor have already decided on their preferred treatment plan.

So we decided to redesign our process at a higher level, at the delivery of care itself. Today, many members of my team and I are on a new journey. We started a new health-care services company called RiseHealth, where we are taking all these great "health plan tools" and applying them as far upstream as we can—at the primary care doctor's office. While we are deploying technology for support, we start by focusing on the process. We remain diligent about what our definition of "value" is and what we are doing to drive it.

I have learned some valuable lessons along the way. First, and most important, process improvement works! As simple as that message is, I have seen firsthand how relatively straightforward process redesign can lead to hundreds of millions of dollars in real value while concurrently establishing platforms for future growth. Groups as diverse as Virginia Mason in Seattle, Washington, and Crucial Care in my hometown of Jacksonville, Florida, are using it to improve their own diverse corners of the health-care system and provide current, living proof of that. Second, you need a plan for realizing and capturing value. My favorite phrase is from a mergers and acquisitions book called *Five Frogs on a Log,* by Mark Feldman and Michael Spratt: "If it doesn't advance a value driver, I'm going to shoot it, sell it, or ignore it." Finally, and important for those of you picking up this book, change requires leadership.

Change is hard. Make it easier on yourself by using the tools in this book to make sure you have a structure for that change, so you can do the hard work of leading. We didn't have a resource like this available to us and had to learn some of these lessons the hard way.

To quote Keith, "There are tools, processes, and structures that can assist leaders and their organizations in executing the vision once they exhibit leadership; but without leaders supporting and persisting, the tools are of questionable value. If leaders lead, the tools have significant value."

Good luck on your process-improvement efforts!

Gino Tenace
President and Chief Operating Officer
RiseHealth

INTRODUCTION

Lean Six Sigma can be, and has been, successfully implemented and sustained in all types and sizes of organizations. It has also failed in many organizations. The question is: What separates the organizations that are successful in deploying Lean Six Sigma from those that are not? The answer is that successful organizations provide the structures and support systems necessary to have a robust, value-added program, whereas the organizations that falter fail to provide the strong foundation necessary for success. This book provides organizational leaders with a clear roadmap of what is required to lay a foundation that ensures Lean Six Sigma success. It lays out what is called the Lean Six Sigma Deployment Roadmap, which takes an organization's leaders through seven sequential phases that enable them not only to successfully implement Lean Six Sigma, but also to sustain the program. It further enables leaders to ensure that Lean Six Sigma evolves from being a program to being woven into the fabric of the company such that it is integrated into the way the organization does business.

This book has four main sections:

Chapters 1–4 cover the conceptual framework and basic concepts of Lean Six Sigma; they discuss Lean Six Sigma as a philosophy as well as a strategy, and also provide an overview of the Lean Six Sigma methodology. The information in these chapters is sufficient to introduce someone who is not knowledgeable about Lean Six Sigma to its major concepts. I don't intend them to be intensely detailed chapters that get into the minute details of the Six Sigma methodology; rather, I intend them to provide a sufficient overview of the subject so that the later chapters on deployment make sense to you.

Chapter 5 describes for you the numerous ways Lean Six Sigma can benefit your organization. While many understand how Lean Six Sigma works as a methodology, not everyone fully understands how Lean Six Sigma benefits an organization. The whole purpose of Lean Six Sigma is to assist leaders in moving the organization forward, increasing value, and delivering results. This chapter provides an overview of the myriad benefits Lean Six Sigma can provide to your organization.

The majority of the book, **chapters 6 through 13**, covers the Lean Six Sigma Deployment Roadmap in detail. Many organizations, when they implement a Lean Six Sigma program, find that the program fails to deliver all the potential benefits I describe in chapter 5. This is in spite of expending significant resources to implement the program. Often, this is not because insufficient resources were invested, but rather they were not properly directed and allocated. The Lean Six Sigma Deployment Roadmap provides organizations the needed vision and direction to ensure success.

The Lean Six Sigma Deployment Roadmap lays out, in detail, the sequential steps that your organization needs to go through in order to successfully implement a Lean Six Sigma program and maximize the return on your investment. Many organizations fail to comprehensively address all of the systems, structures, and needs that are clearly laid out in the Deployment Roadmap. Instead, such organizations attempt to shortcut the deployment process. In an effort to rush to show activity and generate results, the organization gives short shrift to critical elements of the Lean Six Sigma infrastructure. This gives rise to structural flaws within the program, such as unaligned leadership, poor project selection, inadequate Lean Six Sigma team support, redundant efforts creating inefficiencies, and ineffectual communication. These flaws cause substandard and inconsistent results across the organization. When this happens, leadership often questions the effectiveness of the Lean Six Sigma methodology. The problem lies not with Lean Six Sigma or the ability of the methodology to generate results; rather, it is with the lack of systems and structures which would allow the program to be effective and to flourish.

Often, the problem in underperforming programs is not that leaders are underresourcing the Lean Six Sigma effort; rather, the resources are not being optimally applied. The Lean Six Sigma Deployment Roadmap identifies the specific structures, systems, and activities that need to take place and the sequence in which they must occur, so that the organization can apply resources in an optimal fashion in order to derive maximum benefit from the Lean Six Sigma program.

The ultimate result of following the Lean Six Sigma Deployment Roadmap is that Lean Six Sigma transforms from a program into the way your organization does business. If you follow the roadmap, over time, what is initially a program integrates into your organization's culture and becomes part of the way your organization does business every day. If your leadership team is able to successfully implement and sustain a Lean Six Sigma effort such that it becomes embedded in the organization and becomes part of the organizational culture, your leaders will have truly transformed the organization. This book provides your organization's leaders with a roadmap for that journey.

Go to www.e-mri.net/roadmap.htm to download a free, full-color, 24" x 36" or 11" x 17" PDF of the eMRI Lean Six Sigma Deployment Roadmap.

Finally, **chapter 14** details some of the most common pitfalls that organizations experience when attempting to implement Lean Six Sigma. It highlights cultural barriers as well as strategic and process-based issues that often derail implementation efforts and result in underperforming or failed programs.

CHAPTER 1

INTRODUCING LEAN SIX SIGMA

W. Edwards Deming is one of the greatest minds of the past 50 years on the subject of continuous improvement. Back in the 1950s, he contacted a large number of companies regarding continuous-improvement consulting; those companies did not see the value of what Deming offered and told him to "take a hike." So he did—to Japan. Deming then spent over 20 years in Japan working with myriad companies.

In the late 1970s and 1980s, many of the US companies that had told Deming to "take a hike" realized that they had made a mistake and asked him to come back to the United States. One of the companies he came back to and worked with was Ford Motor Company. One of my co-workers at eMRI worked for Ford Motor Company during that period and had the opportunity to work directly with Dr. Deming. One day, in a meeting with my co-worker and his peers, Dr. Deming placed a stack of papers down on a table and announced, "This is a draft copy of a book I'm writing. I'm going to go talk to the senior leadership and explain to them that this is what we're going to do. I thought you might like to see a copy of it so you know what's coming." Needless to say, the group immediately made copies for everybody and they began to voraciously read through it. The title page on the stack of papers read: *Quality, Productivity, and the Competitive Position.*

The title on the draft copy was Deming's overarching message: the key to being successful, in whatever market you serve, is quality and productivity. If you can produce products or services at higher levels of quality and higher levels of productivity than your competition, you will be successful. Deming was a brilliant man, and many of the companies that embraced his teachings back in the '50s, '60s, and '70s have been fantastically successful.

Achieving Deming's message of improving business results through improvements in quality and productivity is the whole purpose of Lean Six Sigma. By combining the benefits of Lean with the strengths of Six Sigma, dramatic improvements can be achieved in organizational performance.

Historically, Lean (originally, Lean Manufacturing) and Six Sigma were viewed as separate routes to continuous improvement. What we call Lean today originated with Toyota around 1950 and was called the Toyota Production System. What we call Six Sigma was created by Motorola and became popular in the late 1980s and early 1990s. What follows is a brief explanation of both Lean and Six Sigma as independent methodologies, culminating in a description of how Lean and Six Sigma merge synergistically, to amplify the benefits each provides independently.

LEAN

Lean, sometimes called Lean Operations, is the name given to what was originally known as the Toyota Production System. Taiichi Ohno conceived the origins of the Toyota Production System in the late 1940s. It is called Lean because it strips the fat out of processes.

Lean focuses on the reduction of waste and the maximization of flow. Waste is anything that does not add value. If something adds value, it is described as a value-added activity; if it does not, it is referred to as a non-value-added activity. For something to be value added, it has to (1) change the form, fit, or function of the product or service and (2) the customer has to be willing to pay for it. If the customer is not willing to pay for it, it is not value added and it is waste.

Flow has to do with the movement of materials and information in the manufacturing or service process. The process is often referred to as the value stream and consists of all the steps necessary to produce the customer-desired output. The customer desires that materials and information flow from step to step without stoppages or delay.

WASTE

We can categorize types of waste using the acronym:

DOWNTIME.

1.01: Eight Types of Waste ◄━━━━━━━━━━━

D ----------► **D**efects
O ----------► **O**verproduction
W ----------► **W**aiting
N ----------► **N**on-utilized resources
T ----------► **T**ransportation
I ----------► **I**nventory
M ----------► **M**otion
E ----------► **E**xcessive processing

Now, let's look at each of these eight types of waste.

Defects

Defects are also known as errors, mistakes, or non-conformities. When defects occur, resources have to be expended to both identify and fix them. Additional resources may have to be expended to compensate customers if the defects are not found internally, before the service or product reaches the customers. If an organization produces defects or mistakes, it may need additional capacity or inventory to meet its customers' needs.

Overproduction

Overproduction is producing more than the customer requires. In a Lean environment, the process produces only what is required by the customer. In manufacturing, overproduction is a chronic problem. Managers often believe that if the plants are not running 100 percent of the time, the company is losing money.

The result is inventory, another form of waste. Overproduction is also a significant problem in many transactional environments. For example, paperwork and electronic information are often produced at a rate that ignores the rate at which the downstream process steps are capable of receiving and processing information.

On the other hand, overproduction is not possible in some service environments because you can produce the service only when the customer directly requests it. It isn't possible for a call center handling customer calls to complete and inventory calls before the calls come in.

Waiting

Anytime that people, equipment, facilities, or anything else is idle, waste is being created or incurred. If a person is waiting for information or for material, the time spent waiting is a form of waste. Likewise if an office building is utilized only eight hours a day and is idle for 16 hours a day, that idle time is a form of waste. In most organizations, assets are utilized only a fraction of the time, which means that waiting is a significant form of waste.

Non-Utilized Resources

One of the tenets of Lean Operations is to fully utilize the organization's resources. For example, a company recently purchased a piece of packaging equipment capable of producing 20 different sizes of packaged products, but uses it to produce only a single package size. This is an underutilized resource.

The company expended a huge sum of money for a highly flexible resource and they are not using any of the flexibility of that resource. Another example is the utilization of people; if an organization has a highly educated and highly trained individual and the organization is not utilizing that education and training, it is waste.

Transportation

Anytime that materials or products are transported, there is waste. Whenever raw materials or finished products are shipped to another location, the transporting is non-value-added activity.

Most people think of transportation as being uniquely associated with manufacturing, but that's not so. Service organizations also have transportation. Examples include documents that are mailed or transported via courier and materials such as legal or accounting documents that need to be transported in and out of storage areas.

Inventory

Inventory is also a type of waste, and it can take many forms. For example, in a manufacturing company, inventory can be raw material, work in progress (WIP), or finished products. Service organizations also often have WIP inventory. Examples of this include paperwork such as bills, invoices, and employment applications.

Hospitals and other health-care providers have vast physical inventories of medical supplies that require working capital to maintain. Examples of inventory found almost everywhere include office supplies such as paper, copier supplies, filing supplies, computer supplies, shipping materials, and all the other materials that most offices require for daily operation.

There is also non-tangible inventory. Look at almost anyone's e-mail inbox and count the number of backlogged e-mail messages. These, too, are inventory, even if they aren't physical.

Motion

Motion is closely related to transportation. However, transportation usually refers to the movement of something between locations, whereas motion is the movement that is required within a specific location.

If a workstation is poorly laid out, either in an office or a manufacturing plant, excessive motion will be required. Examples of motion include having to reach for paperwork, the phone, files, tools, or materials. Poor workplace layout can also result in ergonomic concerns.

Excessive Processing

Anytime a process is performing work that the customer is not willing to pay for, it is excessive processing. Any effort or activity that does not alter the form, fit, or function of the product or service being offered, or any action that the customer is not willing to pay for, is a form of waste.

Many things can cause excessive processing, such as not correctly understanding the customer's needs, lacking adequate employee training, or having unclear rules, policies, and procedures.

SOME WASTE MAY BE UNAVOIDABLE

Before we leave the topic of waste, I'd like to note that saying something is waste doesn't always mean it's unnecessary or that you can avoid it. Waste is anything the customer is not willing to pay for. Unfortunately, many things that are non-value-added are still unavoidable. That is not to say it is desirable, only that it is often not possible to eliminate some waste **now**, as that waste is necessary to meet a customer demand.

Transportation is a form of waste; however, transportation, in many cases, is necessary. For example, many companies produce the masking tape sold in an office supply store in Chicago. One company produces tape in Los Angeles and the tape is shipped to Chicago to be sold; the shipment of tape adds considerable cost for the manufacturer. A second tape manufacturer produces the tape in Chicago, so virtually no transportation is required.

The manufacturer located in Los Angeles cannot charge more for the tape in a retail setting because the equivalent tape from multiple other manufacturers is present in the same retail setting.

Customers will not pay more for one manufacturer's product compared to another's because one of the rolls of tape had to be shipped across the country. The price of a roll of tape is set by the market and is not a function of how far the manufacturer needed to ship the tape.

Most customers do not live directly adjacent to the facilities that produce the products and services that they require. Thus, transportation, while still a form of waste, is necessary in many instances. The goal in these situations is to find ways to minimize the waste. This might be done, for example, by relocating the manufacturing facilities nearer to the customer or by building many smaller facilities instead of maintaining a single large one.

Now that we've discussed the different kinds of waste, I'd like to introduce another aspect of the Lean approach: flow.

FLOW

Flow has to do with the movement of materials and information in the value stream. Lean practitioners seek to maximize flow while simultaneously identifying and eliminating waste.

The first key concept related to flow is the concept of push versus pull. Many organizations have what is termed a *push system*. That is, the processes push product to the next step in the process, regardless of demand. This results in excess inventory at every step of the process. Even if a subsequent process step has no need of additional product or service, the step before keeps producing as much as possible and passing it downstream.

1.02: Push – Maximum Production Regardless of Demand ◄▬▬▬

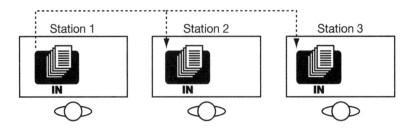

The inventory created by a push system also creates secondary issues. For example, having inventory of work in progress, or WIP, will result in an increase in quality problems and defects. Assume, for example, that a process step pushes product that then sits in an inventory storage area for a period of time before it is used by the next process step. If the product produced by the first process step was defective, this may not be discovered until the inventory of material is used in the next process step, which means that the problem may go undetected for a long period. Thus, if a problem occurs in the first process step, a huge quantity of defective material might be produced and have to be scrapped. If the first process step had not been pushing product into inventory but rather manufacturing to demand, the defective product would have been detected immediately and corrected without having to scrap out a large amount of costly inventory.

The concept of producing only to customer demand is called a *pull system*. In a pull system, each step in the process produces only what is needed by the "customer" of the process step, i.e., the downstream process step.

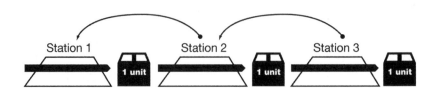

If the "customer" step does not require a product or service, the process step does not provide or create the product or service. A pull system eliminates the inventories seen when a process pushes product or service. As I noted earlier when discussing waste, some types of transactional processes, by their very nature, are pull systems. The example I used earlier to define overproduction was a customer call center. By definition, the customer can only be serviced when the customer calls in. Each call is answered when the phone rings and the center addresses the customer's issue. That being said, many service processes are also push processes. If you have ever witnessed work backing up in someone's inbox or e-mail account, you have witnessed a push system.

That completes your introduction to Lean, so I will now turn to Six Sigma.

SIX SIGMA

Six Sigma, like Lean, drives continuous improvement and improves organizational results. However, the philosophy and methodology of Six Sigma is significantly different from that espoused in Lean.

Six Sigma – Variation Reduction

The goal of Six Sigma is to improve processes to the point where the process output hits the customer's target (whatever it may be) exactly, each time. To accomplish this, it focuses on getting processes centered on the customer's target and then reducing variation so that the process exhibits a minimum amount of deviation from the target; this results in maximum possible customer satisfaction. As its practitioners say, Six Sigma focuses on getting processes "on target with minimum variation." For example, if a manufacturer is to make two parts so that one fits snugly inside the other, it must ensure that both parts meet the target dimensions. If the inserted part is too large, it will be difficult or impossible to insert. If it is made too small, it will not fit snugly and the assembly will fail. There are similar issues with transactions. An airline flight is scheduled between two cities, departing at a specified (target) time every day. If some days it leaves 30 minutes early and other days it leaves 30 minutes late, there will be problems with passengers getting through security in time, making connections, etc. Any variation around the target decreases quality and customer satisfaction.

1.04: Variation Reduction

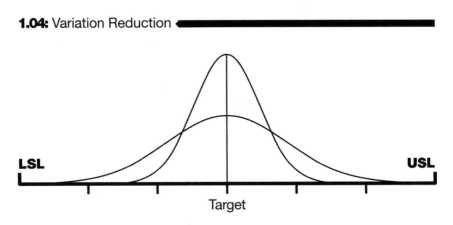

Target

You can see the benefits of variation reduction in figure 1.04. In the figure, the two vertical-line endpoints are the customers' upper and lower requirements (often called the upper and lower specification limits and abbreviated *USL* and *LSL*, respectively). The graphic also shows two bell-shaped curves (this is the shape of a normally distributed process or product, which is the most commonly seen distribution shape). Each of the two curves represents the distribution of product or service that is produced by a process, with the y-axis being the number of products or services. Both of the processes' outputs center exactly on the target value, which is the center of the customer requirements. However, the curves are not identical, as one curve is significantly wider than the other. The wider the curve, the more variation there is in the product. Thus, the narrower of the two curves, because it has less variation, is the better of the two. It will produce product or service closer to the customers' target. The source of the variation in the product is the process. Product behavior follows process behavior. The key to having the product on target is to have the process on target. The key to having minimal variation in the product is to have minimum variation in the process. Whatever behavior is seen in the process will manifest itself in the product.

From a variation-reduction perspective, the process represented by the wider of the two curves is, at best, a marginal process. Viewing the wider of the two curves, one can see that the tips of the curve are exactly on the customers' specifications. This means that the process is only capable of producing product or service that meets the customers' requirements if the process remains perfectly centered on the target. The variation is so large that unless the process is centered on the target value, large amounts of the output will not meet the customers' requirements. If anything happens to negatively affect the process, and the process curve moves to the left or to the right even an iota, a significant proportion of the curve will be outside the customers' requirements. That means that a significant proportion of the process output will fail to meet the customers' requirements.

Viewing the narrower of the two curves, you can see that the tips of the curve are a significant distance from the customers' requirements. As a result, if the process is negatively affected and the curve moves to the left or to the right, it is highly unlikely that the tip of the curve will move outside the customers' requirements. For a tip of the curve to move outside the specifications, the perturbation to the process would have to be extremely large. Thus, we can see that a reduction in process variation (a tighter process distribution) yields improvements in product and service quality, enhances customer satisfaction, and reduces cost to the organization.

However, it is not enough to minimize variation; you must also ensure that the process is on target. As figure 1.05 shows, neither of the two curves centers on the target. Now the right tip of the wider curve is significantly outside of customer requirements, which means that a significant proportion of the service or product produced will fail to meet customer requirements. Even in viewing the narrower curve, which has substantially less variation, we see that the upper tip of the curve is now located exactly on the customers' upper specification limit. If the process is perturbed and shifts even slightly to the right, a portion of the curve will then be outside the customer requirements and the process will produce unacceptable output. Thus, even a process with minimal variation will not produce conforming product unless it centers on the target value. Any shift from the target value increases the probability that the service or product will not meet customer requirements. It is not enough to minimize variation; one must minimize variation around the target value.

1.05: Variation Reduction ◄━━━━━━━━━━━━━━━━━━━

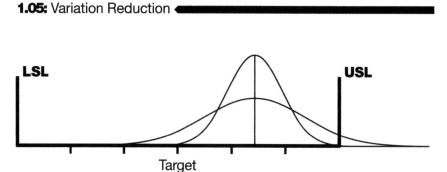

Target

The goal of any organization, of course, is to ensure that 100 percent of the product or service produced not only meets the customer specifications, but is also viewed by the customer as superlative. Thus, Lean Six Sigma practitioners define quality as: "for what is important, on target with minimum variation."

Traditionally, organizations make judgments about their products and services by comparing them to customer requirements. Six Sigma says that it is not sufficient to meet the customers' requirements; what is desired is to hit the customers' target each time. Six Sigma takes this approach because customers do not see quality "as meeting customer requirements." This definition of quality implies that all outputs that fall within the requirements are identical from the customers' perspective and that all outputs that fall outside the requirements are likewise identical. This is not how customers perceive services and products; they see quality as "distance from the target." The closer the product or service comes to the customers' target value, the higher the customers' perception of quality and the higher the level of customer satisfaction.

1.06: Product and Service Quality – Deviation from Target Value ◀━━

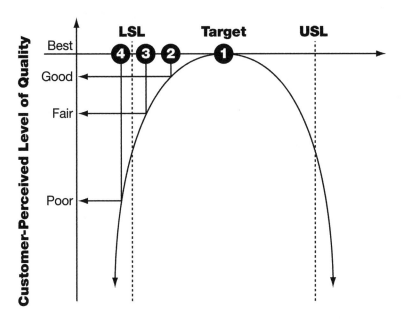

Figure 1.06 illustrates how customers perceive quality. On the horizontal axis, the customers' requirements are shown along with a target value. Note that this target, like most, centers between the upper and lower bounds of the customers' requirements. The vertical axis shows customers' perception of the quality of the product or service and their associated level of satisfaction. The parabolic curve in the figure is what is known as the *quality function*. The quality function connects the produced product or service to the customers' level of satisfaction. To use the quality function, we identify where along the horizontal axis

the product or service offered falls, relative to the target value and requirements. Once you locate that point on the horizontal axis, descend vertically from that point until you contact the quality function curve and then stop. From that exact location on the quality function, move horizontally to the left until you reach the vertical axis (customer satisfaction). This allows you to determine the customers' perception of quality and level of customer satisfaction. The higher the location is on the vertical axis, the higher the customers' level of satisfaction.

Note that figure 1.06 shows four *units of output* numbered one through four. Examining unit one, we see it is exactly on target. Thus, you do not need to descend downward at all to contact the quality function. This unit results in maximum customer satisfaction. Unit two misses the target, but not by much. Some descent is required to contact the quality function, but the level of customer satisfaction is still reasonably high. Unit three misses the target by a more significant margin, resulting in customer satisfaction that is only fair. Unit four is the farthest from target and results in poor customer satisfaction. The quality function shows us that the farther the product or service falls from the target value, the lower the level of customer satisfaction.

To place this concept in context, consider room temperature. Hypothetically, let's say you have a target room temperature of 72°. However, you are realistic in your requirements and specify that the temperature be 72° plus or minus five degrees. If the temperature is 72°, your comfort is optimized. In fact, the closer the temperature is to 72°, the more comfortable you will be. If the room were at 70°, you would be less comfortable than at 72°. At 67°, you would be less comfortable than at 70°. The farther the temperature gets from your target value, the less comfortable you will be, regardless of whether the temperature is inside or outside the specifications. Yet, in spite of customer satisfaction decreasing as the service or product moves further from the target, organizations continue to define quality as meeting customers' requirements. This insistence on defining quality as meeting customers' requirements results in absurd situations.

Continue with the example of room temperature when there is a target of 72° and upper and lower customer requirements of 67° and 77°, respectively. Let's compare the organizational response to two different situations:

- Situation 1 – room temperature = 66.99 degrees (0.01 degree outside the lower customer requirement)

- Situation 2 – room temperature = 67.01 degrees (0.01 degree inside the lower customer requirement)

The difference in the two temperatures above is 0.02 degrees. The human body cannot tell the difference between temperatures that differ by 0.02 degrees. Yet, let's examine the organizational response to each situation:

- Situation 1 – When the customer complains about the temperature, the organization springs into action to fix the situation, as the temperature is outside the specifications.

- Situation 2 – When the customer complains about the temperature, the organization instructs the customer to stop his or her whining, as the temperature meets the specifications.

The customer can't tell the difference between these two situations. Yet the reaction to the complaint will be completely opposite, depending on which happens. To treat the customer differently in these two scenarios is lunacy. Yet, that is exactly how most organizations run their businesses!

Another good example is an experience that all of us have had—waiting in a doctor's office or the office of another health-care provider. Such organizations often set an internal goal for maximum wait time in order to judge their performance. As customers, regardless of arbitrarily established requirements, our target wait time is zero. When we walk in the door, we would like to be served immediately—with zero delay. It doesn't matter what the health-care provider sets as its internally generated target; as customers, the longer it takes before we receive the desired service, the lower our level of customer satisfaction.

Imagine a hospital chain that owns two hospitals and both have an internal requirement that patients be seen in less than 30 minutes. In the first hospital, every emergency room patient waits exactly 29 minutes before being helped. In the second hospital, each patient waits exactly one minute. In both cases, the hospital chain reports 100 percent compliance with the internal standard and the chain judges both hospitals the same—they are excellent. But from the customers' point of view, this is not true. Customers are far more satisfied with a one-minute wait time than a 29-minute wait time. Customers see quality as distance from target, not as meeting an arbitrary specification.

Six Sigma recognizes that customers see quality as distance from target value. Thus, Six Sigma strives to reduce the variation around the optimal value so that dramatic improvements in customer satisfaction, productivity, and quality can be realized. This is why the correct definition of quality used by Six Sigma practitioners is: "for what is important, on target with minimum variation."

MERGING LEAN AND SIX SIGMA

Each of the two programs, when used individually, can yield dramatic results. However, when we use them together, we realize the greatest possible benefit. In spite of this, some practitioners focus exclusively on Six Sigma. They claim that Six Sigma is the ultimate continuous-improvement program. Others focus exclusively on Lean. The problem with both of these approaches is that the organization does not get maximum benefit. To achieve the maximum benefit, we must synergistically integrate the two philosophies or methodologies.

Assume that the organization focuses exclusively on Six Sigma. Six Sigma practitioners strive to reduce the variation in processes so they become on target with minimum variation. If all we do is strive for variation reduction, we run the risk of improving non-value-added process steps. That is, we can focus our improvement efforts on things that the customer is not willing to pay for. Put more bluntly, you run the risk of getting really good at things that add no value. As a result, the company incurs expenses for things the customer will not pay for.

If we focus only on Lean, we can eliminate the waste in the process, but we may not have the tools necessary to ensure that the value-added process steps perform properly. That is, we have a Lean process that eliminates non-value-added steps, but the remaining value-added steps are not capable of hitting the customers' target every time.

As a result, we have poor quality and low levels of customer satisfaction.

A second issue that arises when embracing only Lean is that variation reduction is often necessary to enable Lean efforts. For example, in order to eliminate waste and maximize flow, you may need to reduce the variation in equipment downtime, cycle time, or quality to pull significant amounts of waste of the process. If you don't reduce variation at the same time, then you will need to retain waste (e.g., excess capacity, inventory) to serve as a buffer against the unwanted and detrimental variation.

Finally, the last reason it is advantageous to combine Lean and Six Sigma is that Six Sigma provides the rigor of the DMAIC methodology. DMAIC is the acronym for the sequential five-phase project methodology used by Six Sigma project teams: Define, Measure, Analyze, Improve, and Control.

1.07: DMAIC Methodology ◄━━━━━━━━━━━━━

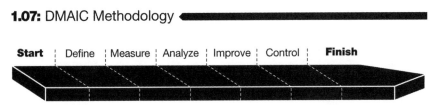

This structured methodology ensures effective and efficient project completion with sustainable process gains. Thus, it is only by combining these two programs together into Lean Six Sigma that one truly gets the maximum benefit.

CHAPTER 2

VALUE STREAMS AND PROCESS THINKING

A key concept in Lean Six Sigma thinking is the concept of *value streams*. A value stream is the chain of functions, activities, or actions that produce the product or service the customer values. A value stream typically involves many different departments or functions. Unfortunately, most organizations don't think in terms of value streams, they think in terms of functions. These functions often operate as if they were silos or chimneys. Figure 2.01 shows both functional silos and the value stream that cuts across them.

2.01: Concept of Value Streams

The problem with functional thinking is that even if the organization undertakes continuous improvement efforts, the efforts are often undertaken independently by each department. No one is looking at the whole system. The result is that one function in a value stream may practice continuous improvement and perform at a very high level, but other functions in the value stream do not. Likewise, the handoffs between functions may not be optimized. The value stream is only as strong as its weakest link. When a problem occurs, the customer does not see departments or functions, the customer sees only the output of the value stream. If customers have a problem with the products or services they have purchased, they don't care which function produces the problem.

For example, imagine that you recently purchased a computer peripheral (e.g., printer, external speakers, or external hard drive) in a store. When you took the device out of the packaging and turned it on, it did not work. As a customer, you would be indifferent to the reason it was not working; whether it was designed improperly, manufactured improperly, transported improperly, or damaged at the store is irrelevant to a consumer. The fact is there was a failure somewhere in the value stream. As customers, we don't care where in the value stream the failure took place. We simply want the product to function. Unless the organization addresses the entire value stream in its continuous improvement efforts, there will likely be no meaningful impact from the customers' perspective.

The concept of the value stream is also important in identifying how to minimize waste and cost. In looking at the whole rather than the parts, it is often apparent that some steps in a process occur more quickly than other steps. It is best that all steps in a process take the same length of time, as this will minimize waste.

Ideally, every step in the process will operate at the *takt time*. The takt time is the rate of customer demand, often measured in units per day or units per shift. If, for example, there are 480 minutes in a working day and the customer requires 100 units per day, the takt time is 4.8 minutes per unit. In optimizing a process, it is best that each of the steps requires exactly the same takt time to complete. If this is accomplished, it eliminates any of the process steps waiting, the buildup of inventory both within the process and of finished product, and potentially other wastes.

This means that slowing down selected process steps can actually be a path to increasing overall process efficiency. If looking only at an individual step, the goal is to always speed up the step, which may be the opposite of what is desired to optimize the entire value stream. Increasing the speed could result in more waiting, increased inventory buildup, more defects, etc.—the antithesis of Lean thinking.

PROCESS THINKING VERSUS PRODUCT THINKING

When I use the term *product thinking*, it refers to the output from the value stream (process). The output can be either tangible, as in the case of manufacturing, or intangible, as in the case of service deliverables. I use the term *product* in this book to describe both tangible and intangible process outputs.

Most organizations are trapped in a product-thinking world. That is, they spend most of their time looking at the output of their processes. In manufacturing, this is referred to as inspection. In service industries, there is typically a similar sort of inspection if there is something tangible such as an invoice or an audit function that periodically looks at the outputs of key processes.

Product-thinking organizations follow the product-control loop. In the product-control loop, the output from the process is looked at and a decision is made as to whether the product is suitable for the customer. This is done by comparing the product to the customers' requirements. If the product does not meet customers' requirements, the organization must fix it. In manufacturing situations, we refer to this remediation as scrapping, reworking, or downgrading. In service industries, we use terms such as remediate, replace, or compensate. Note that oftentimes in transactional environments, it is not possible to inspect the output from the process before it gets to a customer. This makes the concept of product control even weaker as a strategic approach to quality, productivity, and customer satisfaction.

PRODUCT CONTROL

The product-control cycle is shown in figure 2.02. If one views the product-control cycle for service, the output of the process is observed and compared to a product measure of quality, the customer requirements. If the service meets the customer requirements, no action need be taken. If the service does not meet the customer requirements, then some sort of damage control is undertaken. The service can be remediated (made to be conforming through additional work), replaced (redone), or compensation for failure can be offered. In the manufacturing example, the words are slightly different, but the concept is exactly the same. The output of the process is observed or measured and compared to the specs. If it is in spec, the next words heard will be, "Ship it." If it does not meet spec, the product will need to be scrapped (thrown out), reworked (made to be in spec by additional work), or downgraded (sold for less money as a lower-grade product).

A co-worker of mine, Mark, once told me a story that illustrates this point. Years ago, after many years spent in rural Illinois, he and his wife moved to Ann Arbor, Michigan. One of the most significant differences they saw was the price of housing. In order to be able to purchase a home in Ann Arbor, they were forced to downscale significantly and purchase what is generally termed a "handyman's special."

After they spent several years tackling improvement projects one by one, it came time to replace the carpet. They had saved up enough money to replace the carpet on only one floor of the house and they opted to replace the upstairs carpet because the master bedroom carpet had a seam that had become severely split. At the time they purchased the house, the seam was split so badly that there was a three-foot-long hole in the carpet.

2.02: Product (Output) Control

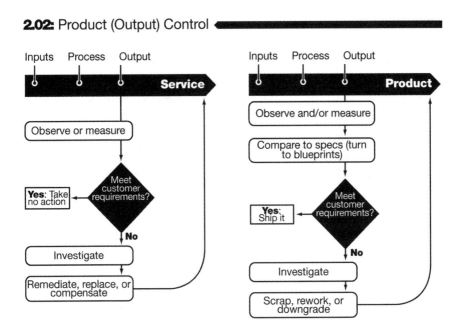

When the store manager came to the house to take the measurement for the upstairs carpet, Mark pointed out the seam in the master bedroom. He specifically stated to the manager that he wanted the seam moved to the other side of the room. That would ensure that the seam was moved from a high-traffic area near the door to a low-traffic area, and thus the new seam should never split. After taking his measurements, the manager told Mark that given the configuration of the room and the width of the carpet they had selected, it would take a couple of extra yards of carpet to move the seam. When taking into account the cost of the carpet, the padding, and the labor, it would cost about $150 to move the seam, which Mark readily agreed to pay.

About a week later, the carpet was installed. Upon arriving home in the afternoon, after the carpet was installed, Mark immediately went to the master bedroom. He arrived at the door of the master bedroom, looked down, and in exactly the same place it had been located before, saw the seam. He rushed to the phone and called the store manager, who drove to the home to view the issue. When the store manager saw the location of the seam, he was mortified.

The manager immediately agreed to replace the carpet in the bedroom if that was desired. However, rather than wait a week or two for new carpeting to arrive and get installed, the carpet store manager proposed a more immediate solution. He proposed to send out an installer with virtually unmatched skill in working with carpet seams, to effectively make the seam invisible. The goal was to improve the seam quality so much that the seam would become invisible and the carpet would not need to be replaced. If Mark was not satisfied with the quality of the work, the carpet would then be replaced.

When Mark and his wife viewed the work done by the installer, they were amazed. The seam had disappeared. Even down on his hands and knees, it took over five minutes for him to locate the reworked seam. The workmanship was incredible. However, as they stood looking at the work, they realized that regardless of the quality of the workmanship, eventually the seam would begin to wear and become visible and, at some point, eventually split. So they contacted the carpet store and requested that the store re-carpet the master bedroom correctly.

The next day, Mark received a call from the carpet store. Apparently, the company was out of that particular carpet and if the store could obtain more carpet, it would have to come from the next lot of carpet the manufacturer produced. The problem with this is that carpet varies from lot to lot in color intensity and other subtleties. So, rather than install carpeting that would not match the rest of the upstairs, the manager proposed to refund the $150 premium to move the seam and rebate another $150 for the inconvenience. Left with no other reasonable options, Mark accepted the offer.

About a year later, the carpet store manager called Mark to ask for a recommendation. Mark's next-door neighbor was going to re-carpet his entire house and the carpet store wished to secure the business. Mark, on learning of the situation, asked the manager a question: "What have you done to change your carpet installation process?" When the manager responded that he had done nothing to change the process, Mark reminded the manager of the problems that he had experienced and informed him he would be sure to share his experiences with the neighbor.

Consider the story in the context of the product-control loop shown in figure 2.03. The service provided was the installation of the carpet and the key customer requirement was the location of the seam in the master bedroom. When the service did not meet the customer's requirements, the first step was to try to remediate the service. When this failed, the store attempted replacement. Finally, when this failed, the store offered compensation.

2.03: Product Control (Reactive Control)◄▬▬▬▬▬▬▬

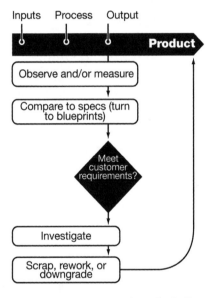

There are three problems associated with following the product-control loop. First, it is purely reactive. Action is not taken until after the problem has already occurred and the customer has been negatively affected. Second, the product-control loop is a very costly way to run an operation. There is the cost of inspection as well as the cost of remediation, both of which significantly reduce productivity and increase cost. Third, nothing has been done to solve the root cause of the problem; tomorrow, exactly the same thing will happen again. If the organization follows the product-control loop, the same problems and issues will continue to occur month after month, year after year.

If an organization simply does enough product control (inspection), it can produce a 100 percent good product from the customers' point of view. In other words, it is possible to achieve customer-perceived quality through inspection. However, given the three problems noted in the previous paragraph, the product-control loop approach degrades overall business performance.

PROCESS CONTROL

Process-improvement experts often define a process as something that creates value. Unfortunately, in my experience, this is sometimes an overly optimistic definition. More generally, a process is something that takes a set of inputs and produces an output. Continuous-improvement experts generally consider that the inputs for every process, regardless of whether it is service or manufacturing, fall into the categories known as the 5Ms: methods, materials, machinery, manpower, and Mother Nature.

In the process-control loop, unlike in the product-control loop, we are not determining whether the product is suitable to give to a customer. As figure 2.04 illustrates, we still take the same information that comes from the observation of the output. But now, instead of evaluating the fitness of the product for sale, we use the information from the output to drive back to the inputs in order to correct any process deficiencies. We do this by comparing the observation or measurement to a process measure of quality, the control limits on a control chart, in contrast to the product-control loop that used a product measure of quality, the customer requirements. The control chart is a statistically based tool which Lean Six Sigma uses to show the behavior of the process. The key is to note that regardless of whether the process is in or out of control, the process-control loop drives back to the process inputs and addresses the root cause of the problem so that it is much less likely to occur again.

Anytime a process output is defective, the problem in the output comes from a problem with one or more of the inputs to the process. If all the inputs are tightly contained around designated targets, the output also will be tightly contained around its target value. The secret to continuous improvement is to stop focusing on the product and focus on the process. If the process is on target with minimum variation, then the product produced by the process also will be on target with minimum variation.

2.04: Process Control (Proactive Control)

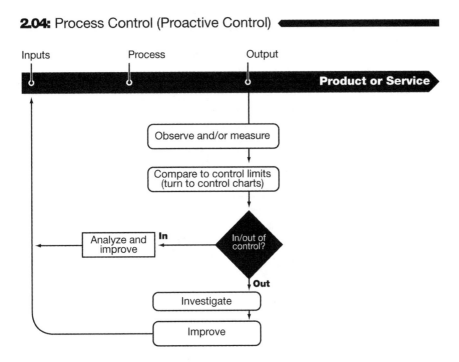

BOTH PROCESS AND PRODUCT CONTROL

Most organizations do both process and product control (figure 2.05); however, product control is primary. That is, the organization focuses the majority of its resources on product control, and process control is an ad hoc activity it uses only when absolutely necessary. Typically, process control is only done when product issues become so large that the organization is forced to send resources upstream to determine the source of the problems. Because of the firefighting mentality that exists in product-control organizations, those tasked with process control are given very little time to generate improvement. Therefore, they slap a short-term fix on the process, a fix that requires minimal time and resources. The problem is that short-term fixes do not remain in place for the long term. The result is a pattern of behavior where you fix the same problems again and again, but never permanently. This is the essence of what some call a *firefighting* organization.

2.05: Process and Product Control Loops

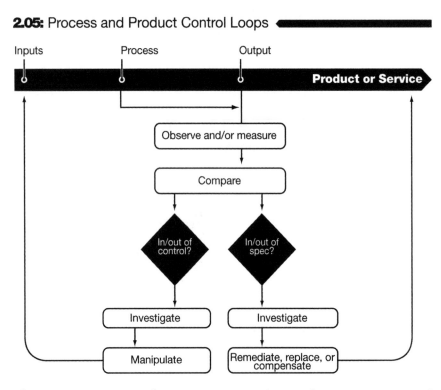

The key to resolving this issue is to evolve so that process control dominates product control. The more process-control activities the organization undertakes, the fewer product problems there will be, so less product control is required. In fact, what is created is an upward cycle whereby process control activities reduce the need for product control, which frees up additional time for more process control, which further minimizes product control, and so on. The result is an organization that has fewer quality problems, lower costs, and higher customer satisfaction. That is not to say that process control will eliminate the need for product control, but it can dramatically reduce it. The more robust the processes become through proactive, preventive process-control activities, the less product control will be required.

You should also note that neither process control nor product control will be successful unless the organization "closes the loop." As graphic 2.06 illustrates, the lines connecting the activities that constitute each loop are broken. One way this commonly happens with process-control loops is this: The organization collects relevant data, but instead of using that data to investigate and improve the process, the organization puts the data in a file cabinet or on a computer hard drive, never to be seen again. This can happen no matter how rigorously staff collect, analyze, and report the data.

2.06: Broken Process and Product Control Loops

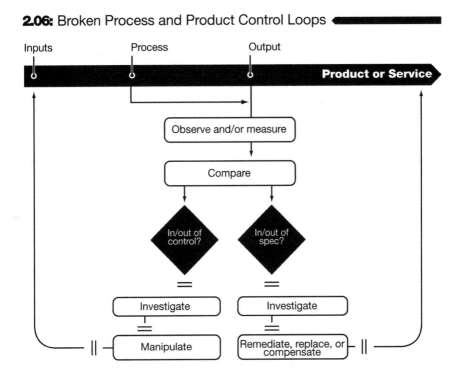

If the organization can mature from a product-control philosophy to a process-control philosophy, it can make vast improvements in productivity and quality. One way to illustrate the effect that process control can have on an organization is process capability. Figure 2.07 shows the relationship between process versus product thinking and process capability. The vertical axis is the capability of the process as measured by two commonly used indices, sigma level (left) and Cpk (right). We don't need to go into the details of how we calculate these commonly used capability indices here. For now, it is enough to note that higher process capabilities imply lower levels of mistakes, errors, or defects (shown as parts per million nonconforming, or ppms), and thus higher levels of quality and productivity. Typically, product-focused organizations are capped at a capability of around three sigma; they produce 66,800 defects or errors per one million units produced. That equates to around 6–7 percent defective service or product.

If the organization can evolve to a process focus, the sigma level it can achieve will be in the four- to five-sigma range. At four sigma, the level of defects or errors is around 0.6 percent, which is roughly a tenfold reduction. At five sigma, the rate of error or defect production is 0.02 percent of product or service produced, a reduction of 99.7 percent from a three-sigma product-control process. Most organizations, when they first evolve to process control, continue to focus on the assessment of the process output (the product). As they mature, they evolve into a more proactive, preventive approach, which is to move upstream from the output and measure the process itself or even the process inputs. Moving upstream to be more proactive results in higher levels of quality and productivity. Not only does the organization reduce defects and errors further, it identifies them earlier in the process, meaning that fixing the problem is cheaper and easier, as it has done less value-added work. Finally, if the organization fully embraces Lean Six Sigma for design functions as well as process functions, the organization can achieve six-sigma levels of performance, which is 3.4 errors or defects per million units of service or product it produces.

2.07: Organizational Philosophy Drives Results ◄━━━━━━

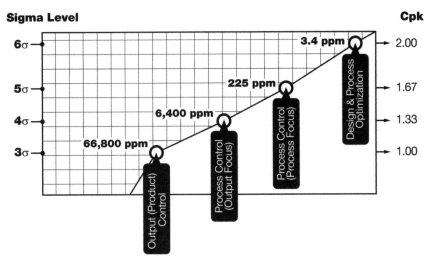

In adopting Lean Six Sigma, the organization will evolve its philosophy, its business strategy, and the methodology by which it improves processes (figure 2.08). Philosophically, the organization moves from product (output) control to process control, and eventually to process optimization. Strategically, it maximizes profitability through improvements in productivity, quality, and customer satisfaction, which it accomplishes by eliminating non-value-added activities and time, and getting value-added activities on target with minimum variation.

2.08: Lean Six Sigma: Philosophy, Strategy, Methodology ◄━━━━━

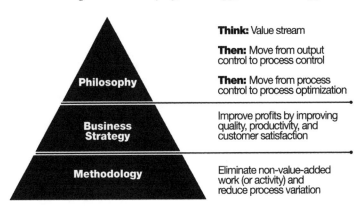

CHAPTER 3

ROLES AND RESPONSIBILITIES

The intent of this chapter is to provide a high-level overview of the roles and responsibilities required for a successful Lean Six Sigma program. In subsequent chapters that deal specifically with different phases of the Deployment Roadmap, I will provide more detailed information on the responsibilities entailed by each role and the skills needed for the various positions.

LEADERSHIP

The most important role is that of organizational leadership. Without proper leadership support, any initiative is doomed to failure. It is the senior leadership team that is ultimately responsible for the success or failure of a Lean Six Sigma program. If leadership is truly supportive of the initiative and the right foundation is laid for success (e.g., the Deployment Roadmap is followed), then the program will be a strong contributor to moving the organization forward and to achieving its business goals and objectives.

Leadership's role can be summarized as directly heading the effort to align the cultural and strategic components of the program and resourcing the process component. If cultural alignment or change is required, this effort must be led by the senior-most people in the organization. It is not possible to drive change in this area unless leadership is actively involved. Likewise, leadership must take direct responsibility for strategic alignment. If there are strategic gaps or conflicts that relate to the implementation of Lean Six Sigma, those who control the strategic direction must assume responsibility for alignment.

Leaders are also responsible for empowering and supporting the deployment teams during implementation and the steering committee after the program has become established. A member of senior leadership should head both the top-level deployment team and the steering committee.

DEPLOYMENT TEAMS

A deployment team is responsible for leading and guiding the implementation of Lean Six Sigma within the deployment team's area of responsibility. The team's responsibilities can be summarized as creating a detailed project plan for implementation and then overseeing or undertaking the specific tasks laid out in the plan. The team will, of course, design its plan to ensure that it will successfully complete all the necessary activities specified in the Deployment Roadmap.

3.01: Deployment Team Org. Chart ◀━━━━━━━━━━━

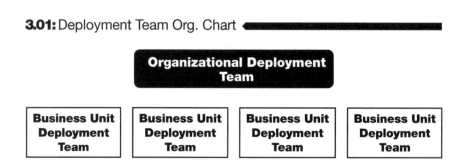

In larger organizations, there may be multiple deployment teams. For example, as shown in figure 3.01, there might be a top-level organizational deployment team as well as business unit deployment teams. Such a structure helps prevent the top-level team from becoming resource starved. Even more important, it lets each business unit have direct input and control of the Lean Six Sigma initiative within the strategic confines specified by the leadership and its top-level deployment team. This provides some strategic independence as well as a high level of tactical independence.

STEERING COMMITTEES

The steering committee is responsible for the ongoing management, assessment of, and improvement of an established and active Lean Six Sigma program. Some of the same people who are on the steering committee may also be on deployment teams. However, the tasks and responsibilities of the steering committee are quite different from those of the deployment teams. The level of resources necessary to support the steering committee is also often lower than that required to support the deployment efforts, as the steering committee is typically concerned with maintenance, control, and improvement, rather than creation and development.

There may be multiple steering committees present. For example, analogous to what was seen for deployment teams in figure 3.01, there may be an organizational-level steering committee as well as business unit steering committees.

CHAMPIONS

Champions are the people who select the Lean Six Sigma projects and provide the resources necessary to support them. Due to their responsibilities, Champions must be relatively senior managers within the organization. Only those who have control of the necessary resources and the ability to eliminate barriers for the team can effectively serve in the role of project Champion. Because the Champions select the projects, resource the projects, and are responsible for removing barriers, they are ultimately held accountable for project success or failure.

BLACK BELTS

Black Belts are responsible for leading Lean Six Sigma project teams. Often, they are referred to as agents of change. They are expected to have detailed knowledge the DMAIC methodology and the tools and methods that are part of that methodology. Black Belts are also responsible for coaching and mentoring Green Belts and team members as well as identifying high-potential people for advancement to the next level within the Lean Six Sigma program. Black Belts typically receive 20 days of training to provide the requisite skills.

GREEN BELTS

Green Belts are, in a sense, junior Black Belts. They typically receive 10 days of training in the Lean Six Sigma methodology. Green Belts may lead Lean Six Sigma project teams; and they sometimes support the Black Belts that manage the teams. Whether a Green Belt is capable of heading a Lean Six Sigma team is primarily a function of project complexity. If the project is one that you do not expect to require Black Belt–level skills, then it is perfectly appropriate for a Green Belt to lead the team. However, if the project is more complex and will likely require the use of Black Belt–level continuous-improvement tools, it is not appropriate for a Green Belt to lead the team, but rather to support the Black Belt who is in charge.

PROJECT TEAM MEMBERS

Project team members are process experts who support the Lean Six Sigma project teams. It is not necessary for the Green Belt or Black Belt managing the project team to be knowledgeable on the process to be improved. The Green Belt or Black Belt only needs to be an expert in the DMAIC methodology. As long as the Green Belt or Black Belt is paired with people who are knowledgeable on the process, they can lead the team through the DMAIC methodology and successfully complete the project. Within our consultancy, we have worked with organizations in industries as diverse as the military, steel manufacturing, call centers, adhesives, supermarkets, medical devices, and logistics. None of our eMRI Black Belts has direct experience in these areas, but we have always been successful in managing and completing Lean Six Sigma projects because we have been supported by process experts.

CHAPTER 4

THE DMAIC PROCESS

All Lean Six Sigma projects follow a five-phase process normally summarized by the acronym DMAIC, which stands for Define, Measure, Analyze, Improve, and Control. Lean Six Sigma projects follow all five of these phases in exactly that order. It is critical to every project's success that the Black Belt or Green Belt leading the team does not shortcut the process or omit any of the critical steps in any of the phases. Shortcutting the DMAIC process creates significant risk of project failure.

4.01 The Lean Six Sigma Methodology

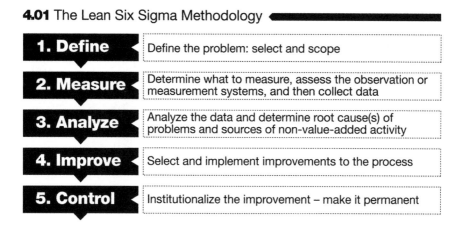

1. Define	Define the problem: select and scope
2. Measure	Determine what to measure, assess the observation or measurement systems, and then collect data
3. Analyze	Analyze the data and determine root cause(s) of problems and sources of non-value-added activity
4. Improve	Select and implement improvements to the process
5. Control	Institutionalize the improvement – make it permanent

DEFINE

The Define phase of a Lean Six Sigma project is concerned with the definition and scoping of the project. This is a very critical stage, as failure to clearly define or to correctly scope the project will result in an increased risk of project failure. The Define phase of the project is analogous to the foundation of a house. If a foundation is not well laid, how well the rest of the house is built is irrelevant; the house is not structurally sound and it will fail. Likewise if a Lean Six Sigma project is not well defined and scoped, it does not matter how smart or how hard-working the Black Belt or Green Belt is; there is a high likelihood of project failure. Even if the project succeeds, if it is ill-defined or poorly scoped, there is still a significant risk that it will fail to meet leadership's expectations and will provide substandard returns.

The most common problem in the Define phase is that the project scope is too large. There is a propensity to overreach and to underestimate the time and resources necessary to solve a problem. When the scope is too large, the project takes longer, and with increased duration comes risk. The longer the project takes, the more impatient management becomes. The risk of conflicting demands for resources increases, as does the risk of competing priorities. It is better to scope projects in a reasonable and rational way that minimizes project risk. There is an old expression that says, "You can't boil the ocean." That is, you can't build a fire large enough to boil the ocean all at once. But you can build a fire large enough to boil a pot of water and over time one can boil an ocean's worth of water one pot at a time. There is wisdom in this old expression when it comes to Lean Six Sigma. Rather than having one large project that will take a long time to complete and have a high risk of failure, break the problem down and tackle it one piece at a time.

MEASURE

Everyone thinks of the Measure phase as collecting data. It is true that the Measure phase does involve the collection of data; but it is actually the last thing that happens, not the first. The first thing done in the Measure phase is to ask, "What data do we require to solve the problem?" Notice that the question was not, "What data is available" or "What data is easy to obtain." The question was, "What data do we need to solve the problem?" Often, when the team determines what data is required, it is immediately apparent that the data needed is not currently collected. At this point, the team will have to pause to develop data collection processes to support the project. While doing so will require resources, there is no choice. If the data the organization had were sufficient to allow the problem to be solved, it likely would have been solved already. The fact that it is still a problem suggests that all the information needed to solve the problem is not currently available.

The other major task in this phase is that the team needs to assess the measurement systems to ensure they are "trustworthy." That is, they must ensure that whatever data comes from the measurement systems represents the true value of whatever is being measured or observed. It does not matter whether the measurement system is a person, a gauge, or a computer system. Just because a measurement system is producing data does not necessarily mean it is producing trustworthy data. Many organizations have a lot of data available, but the data is often not trusted.

As an example, one of our academic partners, the University of North Florida, hosts "breakfast briefings" for executives, on various topics of interest and we occasionally do one on Lean Six Sigma. When explaining to such a group how Lean Six Sigma works, we often ask the audience, "How many of you believe all the data you are shown about your organization and its performance?" In all the years of doing this, when asking for a show of hands, I have yet to see a single hand go up. The problem, of course, is that the executives I am talking with are using the data they don't trust to make decisions and to chart the strategic direction of their company. The cliché "garbage in, garbage out" has never been more appropriate; the decisions an executive makes will be no better than the data he or she has to work with. It is the same with a Lean Six Sigma project; if the team is working with data that is not "trustworthy," the team will make erroneous decisions and the problem remains unsolved.

The team will use a set of statistical tools specifically designed to check the measurement systems providing the data to be used to solve the problem. Once the team has assessed and fixed any measurement systems in need of improvement, it can begin collecting data.

Both leaders and Champions need to recognize that the Measure phase is most often the most challenging phase for project teams. First, the team must determine what data or observations are necessary to identify the root cause of the problem. Often, the team discovers that the data required isn't being collected, so it needs to create new measurement systems. This is a potentially time-consuming activity. Next, even if measurement systems already exist, measurement-system assessments may show that the data these measurement systems produce is not trustworthy. When this happens, the measurement systems must be improved or replaced. Again, this is a time-consuming activity. Figure 4.02 illustrates the challenge associated with the Measure phase.

4.02: DMAIC vs. Level of Despair

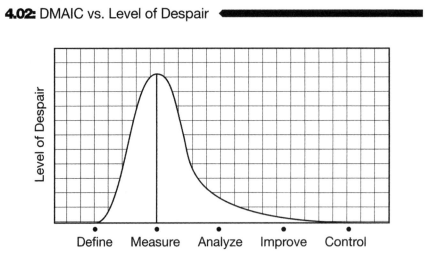

Black Belt and Green Belt training uses figure 4.02 to warn the project leaders about hardships that teams often encounter during the Measure phase and the need for them not to become discouraged by what seem to be repeated setbacks in the project due to measurement difficulties. Such setbacks are part of the process. As the organization matures and becomes more data driven, the difficulties experienced in the Measure phase diminish.

ANALYZE

The Analyze phase is where the team determines the root cause of the problem. Lean Six Sigma teaches us that if we have a problem with a service or product, it is caused by a problem with the process inputs. This is the phase where the team will make the determination as to which inputs are the root causes of the problem to be solved.

If a patient goes to the doctor with a fever and the doctor asks, "What is the problem?" the patient would likely answer, "I have a fever." Unfortunately, that is not the problem, it is a symptom. If the doctor merely treats the symptom by instructing the patient to take some aspirin, the problem will be back every four hours.

What is needed is a diagnosis of the root cause, say, strep throat, and an antibiotic to treat the root cause, which is an infection. You would never tolerate the doctor treating the symptom, yet that is what we do repeatedly in many workplaces. We treat the symptom to temporarily lower the level of pain and then express astonishment when the problem resurfaces … repeatedly. I referred to this earlier as "slapping a short-term fix" on the process, where employees never take the time to fix the problem properly, and therefore the problems keep reappearing.

IMPROVE

The Improve phase is what it sounds like—once you know what the problem is, fix it. However, it is a bit more complex than just "fix it." First, the fix must be one that is long-term and permanent; it cannot be a short-term fix where the problem can recur. It must also be a fix that addresses the root cause, not only the symptoms.

It is in this phase that Lean tools come into play and add tremendous value. Lean tools and methods focus on generating process improvement. Lean techniques such as 5S (organizational housekeeping), standardized work, and visual management—to name a few—improve the performance of a process. The purpose of each Lean tool is to reduce waste and improve flow in the value stream. When you apply them together to a value stream, Lean methodologies can yield tremendous benefit in the Improve phase.

This phase can also be challenging for a Lean Six Sigma team because this is when the process owners see changes being made, and change is often difficult for people to accept. Making change requires the commitment not only of the project team, but also of the Champion.

The other important thing that the team does in this phase is to verify the effectiveness of the improvements made. It is not sufficient to make a change; the team must verify that the change had the desired effect relative to the project goal. If the improvements made to the process do not have the desired impact, Lean Six Sigma requires the team to develop and implement additional improvement strategies. Note that the verification of improvement also includes quantifying the gains to the organization so the team can report them to senior leadership as part of overall program monitoring.

CONTROL

The Control phase of the project is where the team institutionalizes project gains and makes them permanent. One of the failures in many other continuous-improvement methodologies is that the gains are not permanent. Time and time again, processes are improved, only to revert to their prior state. If the process reverts, the organization does not benefit from the improvement effort. In the Control phase, teams undertake a series of tasks to ensure that when the process is turned over to the process owners, it does not revert to its prior state.

The Control phase is often the second-most-challenging phase of the DMAIC methodology. Teams must resist the natural desire to move to the next project before ensuring that the gains from the current project are permanent. When people see the gains, the natural inclination is to want to immediately move forward to the next project to obtain more benefit. However, failure to address the Control phase before moving on to the next project jeopardizes the ability of the organization to sustain the gains. If the process changes unravel and the process reverts to its prior state in a matter of months, the project has effectively yielded no benefit. Shortcutting the Control phase can undo all the hard work of the prior phases.

DMAIC OVERLAY ONTO PROCESS CONTROL

The DMAIC methodology facilitates tracing the process-control loop. Following the DMAIC methodology will ensure that the team completes the process-control loop most efficiently and effectively. As you can see in figure 4.03, each phase of the Lean Six Sigma methodology addresses a specific part of the loop.

WHEN LEAN SIX SIGMA SHOULD BE USED AND NOT USED

Lean Six Sigma is not the solution to all organizational problems. Generally, Lean Six Sigma lends itself well to complex problems where the rigor of the DMAIC methodology is needed, or the vast array of improvement tools and methods that are part of Lean Six Sigma need to be brought to bear. When solving a problem requires the collection and analysis of data using tools such as statistical process control, hypothesis testing, or designed experiments, Lean Six Sigma is an ideal method. Many issues are not that complex. If the problem is not complex, often a simpler problem-solving methodology is better. In other instances, people sometimes propose applying the Lean Six Sigma methodology to issues where the solution is already known. If the solution is known, then fixing it is merely a matter of execution. In this case, just fix it.

4.03: The Lean Six Sigma Integrated Model ◄━━━━━━━━

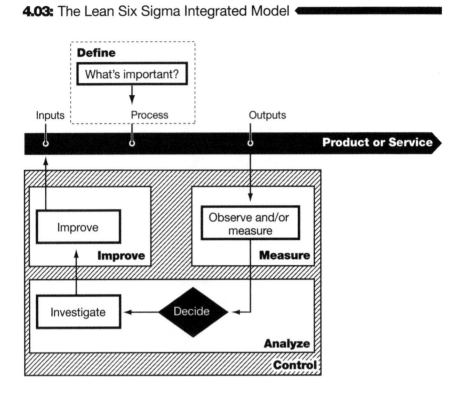

No Free Lunch

Organizations get out of Lean Six Sigma what they put into it. If the organization provides adequate resources to the initiative relative to its goals, the results will be dramatic. However, if the effort is starved for resources, the results will be scant. Under no circumstances should Lean Six Sigma be viewed as a free lunch; you don't get something for nothing. Insufficient resources take two forms:

- insufficient resources for program support, and
- insufficient resources for project support.

When the program has insufficient resources, leadership attempts to shortcut the Deployment Roadmap to avoid investing in the processes and systems needed to ensure both implementation success and long-term sustainability. The motivation for doing this could be time pressure to show results or a desire to minimize resource requirements. Regardless of motivation, the result will be a Lean Six Sigma initiative that underperforms or fails.

Inadequate project support often manifests as inadequate time for the Black Belt or Green Belt, along with their team members, to work on the project. Too often, competing priorities detract from the ability of the Green Belt or the Black Belt to work on the project. The result is that project durations stretch out, leading to management questioning the benefit of the methodology. This can result in declining management support, leading to a negative cycle of failure and ever-declining support. This scenario is most often encountered when the Champions have not been properly educated on how to support the project teams or when the organizational culture is one of firefighting. If the established culture is one of firefighting, then Champions need to ensure that the teams are adequately shielded from being consumed by firefighting activities. This requires a discipline that many find challenging in light of organizational pressures. This is an area that the leadership needs to be sensitive to in terms of aligning the organizational culture.

4.04: Important vs. Urgent ◄━━━━━━━━━━━━━━━━━━━━━

	Important	**Not Important**
Urgent	"Firefighting" Customer deadlines	E-mail Meetings Interruptions
Not Urgent	Lean Six Sigma Long-term planning Relationship building	Gossip Surfing the Internet Spam

This highlights a key challenge that everyone in the organization will face in implementing and using Lean Six Sigma. Stephen R. Covey, in his book, *The 7 Habits of Highly Effective People*, categorizes various activities in a two-dimensional table similar to that shown in figure 4.04. Each day, people are naturally drawn into the quadrants that contain urgent activities. Activities that are not urgent are postponed to a later date. Lean Six Sigma falls into the quadrant that is important but not urgent. The result is that those tasked with implementing Lean Six Sigma, or for using the methodology for process improvement, face a challenge: how to discipline themselves and the rest of the organization to spend time in the important but not urgent quadrant.

If the organization can discipline itself to spend time in the important but not urgent quadrant, working on long-term process improvement, then less time will be required for firefighting. The organization can then use the time saved from the reduced level of firefighting to increase the amount of time spent in the lower left-hand quadrant, further accelerating continuous-improvement activities. In essence, a feedback loop is created: the more time that is spent in proactive, preventive activities, the less time need be spent firefighting, and these newly available resources can be dedicated to increasing the rate of proactive improvement.

The cultural challenge is that the organization must discipline itself to spend the time in the important but not urgent quadrant.

CHAPTER 5

WHY LEADERSHIP SHOULD EMBRACE LEAN SIX SIGMA

In this chapter, I discuss seven reasons why leaders should choose Lean Six Sigma:

- Value creation
- Productivity, quality, and customer satisfaction
- Financial impact
- Structured methodology
- Fitness for all types of organizations
- Quantified gains
- Track record of success

VALUE CREATION

The leadership team of every organization is tasked with creating value. One could define value in a public corporation, for example, as stock market capitalization relative to comparable companies. With respect to a nonprofit social service agency, the definition of value could be the volume and proportion of positive outcomes or benefit to the local community. The point is that while there are many definitions, leadership's responsibility is to increase value. Value can come from many sources. For example, it can be created through innovation in the development of new products or new technologies, or the development of human capital (employees).

In the context of Lean Six Sigma, you create value through the delivery of higher levels of productivity, quality, and customer satisfaction. This means higher levels of quality and productivity in all areas of the organization.

For example, you can apply Lean Six Sigma in the product development area to speed time to market or increase the proportion of successfully developed products. Likewise, you can apply it to the human resources function to decrease turnover or to increase the effectiveness of employee compensation programs. You can also apply it to back office functions such as accounts receivable, to improve cash flow. In fact, Lean Six Sigma can be successfully applied to any area of the organization.

In each area of the organization, you only have to ask the question, "What is important?" Once we understand what is important, we eliminate non-value-added activity and time (waste) associated with the important processes and then get the remaining value-added steps on target with minimum variation. In this way, Lean Six Sigma can enhance the key processes (e.g., product development) that create value for the organization, thus magnifying its benefit beyond the obvious increases in efficiency and reductions in cost.

Another, starker, rationale for embracing Lean Six Sigma is that many leaders work in organizations that are facing an increasingly competitive environment, often with declining resources. Regardless of whether one works for a private corporation, public corporation, nonprofit or governmental agency, resources are constrained, yet demands are increasing and organizational performance must improve if the organization is to remain viable.

Many leaders work for public or private corporations that have numerous competitors. For those corporations to remain in business, they must produce products or services at higher levels of quality and higher levels of productivity than their competition. Even if a corporation is the industry leader in terms of quality and productivity, its competitors are striving to pass it and become the industry leader. This means that in order to maintain an advantage over its competitors, the organization must accelerate the rate at which it improves quality and productivity so that its rate of improvement is faster than its competitors'. If it is not, then the competition will eventually catch and pass the organization in terms of competitive position.

Conversely, if your organization is not the industry leader in quality and productivity, then in order to survive long term, you need to improve quality and productivity at a rate that is faster than the competition, and close the competitive gap. If your rate of improvement is slower than that of the industry leaders, the competitive gap will widen.

In addition to creating value, Lean Six Sigma has myriad other attributes that provide incentives for organizations to adopt it as their methodology for driving continuous-improvement activities:

- It improves productivity, quality, and customer satisfaction.
- It improves financial performance.
- It follows a proven and structured methodology (DMAIC).
- It will work with any type of organization.
- Gains can be proven, quantified, and tracked.
- It has an extensive record of success.

PRODUCTIVITY, QUALITY, AND CUSTOMER SATISFACTION

Three of the keys to organizational success are quality, productivity, and customer satisfaction. If quality, productivity, and customer satisfaction are high, the organization will be poised for financial success. That is not to say that having high levels of quality, productivity, and customer satisfaction guarantees financial success. If leadership makes unwise acquisitions, overleverages the company, or enters the wrong market segments, even the most efficient company can be financially ruined. However, even the most strategically adept company, if it cannot compete on either cost or quality, is likely doomed.

5.01: Productivity, Quality, and Customer Satisfaction

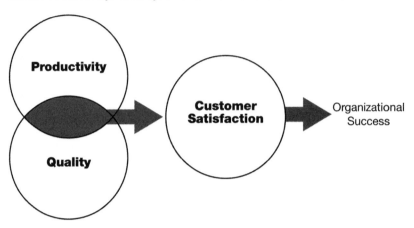

Productivity – Productivity is the ratio of outputs over inputs. The more outputs the process produces and the fewer inputs it requires, the higher its productivity. Outputs are the services or products the process produces. Inputs are the materials, people, equipment, facilities, etc., required to produce the output.

Quality – Quality is defined as "for what is important, on target with minimum variation." What is important and the target value are defined by the customer. Figure 1.06 illustrates the concept of variation reduction.

Customer Satisfaction – Customer satisfaction is a measure of how products or services that the organization supplies meet or exceed customer expectations. Levels of quality and productivity are inputs into customer satisfaction. Customer satisfaction is, in turn, an input into customer loyalty and repeat purchase activity.

It is easy to see how Lean Six Sigma can improve organizational results through improvements in these three key areas. The elimination of waste will improve productivity and also have an impact on quality and customer satisfaction. Getting processes on target with minimum variation will improve quality and customer satisfaction and also have an impact on productivity. These benefits are defined more specifically below.

FINANCIAL IMPACT

A reduction in waste has several immediate financial benefits, including:

- reductions in working capital required through lower levels of inventory;
- improved cash flow through reduced cycle times and increased inventory turns;
- increased capacity through reduced cycle times;
- reduced need for space and facilities through improved productivity and layout; and
- improved bottom-line profits through reduced costs associated with waste.

Likewise, reducing variation in processes will result in improved organization results, including:

- reduced costs through fewer defects and thus less rework, scrap, and customer compensation;
- reduced cost through lowered need for inspection;
- increased revenue through higher rates of repeat purchase created from improved customer satisfaction; and
- improved capacity through reduced defects and reduced rework.

Consider the logic of Lean Six Sigma: Common sense tells us that it is less expensive to proactively prevent a problem from happening in the first place than to pay for the remediation required to fix the problem afterward. This cost efficiency is magnified by the fact that, in most cases, the underlying root cause is never properly addressed, so the organization will incur remediation costs repeatedly.

STRUCTURED METHODOLOGY

Over the years, organizations have tried many different continuous-improvement programs. Most programs advocated the use of continuous-improvement tools and methods, but there was no defined structure that delineated which tools to use in a particular situation, what sequence the tools should be used in, or how to use multiple tools together synergistically to magnify the benefit. The result was that people received training in continuous-improvement tools, but they lacked the framework necessary to ensure that the tools generated continuous improvement. As a result, organizations often perceived the tools as ineffective. Actually, the problem was the lack of a structure for the sequential and synergistic use of the tools and methods. Lean Six Sigma addresses this shortcoming seen in other programs.

All Lean Six Sigma projects follow the Define, Measure, Analyze, Improve, and Control (DMAIC) methodology. Within each phase there is a set of tools, techniques, methods, and documents that teams use to successfully complete that portion of the project. Furthermore, there is a logical sequencing to the use of the tools and techniques. Thus, practitioners are not left to guess what to do next. Just as leaders follow the Leadership Deployment Roadmap, Black Belts and Green Belts follow the DMAIC Roadmap.

FITNESS FOR ALL TYPES OF ORGANIZATIONS

Lean Six Sigma has been implemented by organizations of all types and sizes; private and public corporations, nonprofits, and public sector organizations have all created value using Lean Six Sigma. With the advent of the Internet, the diversity of organizations embracing Lean Six Sigma is quickly apparent. In terms of our consultancy, we have worked with a large diversity of market sectors, a subset of which I present in figure 5.02.

Not only does Lean Six Sigma apply to all sectors in both the service and manufacturing arenas, but it also can work in any size organization. The smallest organization we have ever worked with had seven employees and revenue measured in hundreds of thousands of dollars annually, and the largest had over 100,000 employees and $100 billion per year in revenue.

5.02: Industries Served ◄━━━━━━━━━━━━━━━━━━━━

Manufacturing	Service Industries
• Automotive	• Health care
• Chemicals	• Federal government
• Food	• State government
• Metals	• Real estate
• Semiconductor	• Military
• Electronics	• Engineering
• Furniture	• Utilities
• Medical	• Staffing services
• Computers	• Education
• Printing	

QUANTIFIED GAINS

At the beginning of every Lean Six Sigma project, the team must explicitly state and quantify the project goal. The goal could be a cost savings, cycle time reduction, customer satisfaction improvement, capacity increase, or any other benefit which leaders select. Later, in the Improve phase of the Lean Six Sigma project, the project team is required to verify the effectiveness of the improvements made and quantify the gain relative to the project goal. This quantification is done through the collection and analysis of data, not opinion, to ensure the gains are objectively determined. Typically, the finance department has a representative involved to ensure that the gains are properly computed.

The project-based nature of Lean Six Sigma makes it possible to calculate the gains from each project and then sum the gains across all projects. Thus, leaders can periodically review the program and see both the cost and the benefit of the program. While it is not possible to connect all project benefits directly to a specific dollar value, enough projects will have direct cost savings such that the benefit of the program will be seen to exceed its cost by many, many times. The quantification of program value is something that is not easy to do with most quality programs. For example, if you are asked to determine the financial benefit to the organization of implementing a quality system such as ISO 9000, you will find it virtually impossible. This is not to say that a properly designed and implemented ISO system does not yield benefits, only that computing the financial benefit is extremely difficult.

RECORD OF SUCCESS

Thousands of companies of all types and sizes have successfully used Lean Six Sigma to complete hundreds of thousands of projects. Leadership knows that when it adopts Lean Six Sigma, it is embracing a global continuous-improvement philosophy and methodology with decades of proven success.

This record of success stands in contrast to most continuous-improvement programs, which tend to come and go in relatively brief periods of time. Other continuous-improvement programs, such as Total Quality Management and Quality Circles, have come and gone in recent decades. They tend to gain in popularity and then decline after only a few years. Lean thinking has been around since the 1950s and became popular outside Japan in the 1990s with the publication of *The Machine That Changed the World: The Story of Lean Production*, by Womack, Jones, and Roos. Six Sigma has been publicized for roughly the same length of time. In both cases, the methodologies have been increasing in popularity for over 20 years. This continued increase in acceptance stands in contrast to the brief period of acceptance experienced by most other continuous-improvement programs seen in recent decades.

The bottom line is that Lean Six Sigma has an unrivaled record of increasing organizational value and improving business results across an incredible diversity of organizations. For this reason, Lean Six Sigma has become widely accepted as the leading continuous-improvement methodology in the world today.

CHAPTER 6

THE LEAN SIX SIGMA DEPLOYMENT ROADMAP

When a Lean Six Sigma program delivers lackluster results, leadership sometimes questions the effectiveness of the methodology. Often, the problem lies not with Lean Six Sigma or the ability of the methodology to generate results; rather, it is with the lack of support for the processes and systems that will allow the program to be effective and to flourish. The Lean Six Sigma Deployment Roadmap provides leadership with a clear set of required steps and activities to ensure that Lean Six Sigma delivers the maximum benefit to the organization. It ensures that the organization undertakes the necessary actions and sets up the necessary infrastructure in an organized and timely fashion to optimize Lean Six Sigma success. It does this by not only addressing process issues and infrastructure, but also by addressing the issues of organizational culture and strategy.

CULTURE, STRATEGY, AND PROCESSES

Whenever an organization considers launching a Lean Six Sigma program, three main elements need to be addressed: culture, strategy, and processes.

Culture – Culture is the set of behaviors and beliefs that characterize an organization. Culture influences the way in which people behave, their ethics, level and method of communication, the way they treat others, etc.

Strategy – Strategy consists of two key parts. First, it entails a leadership vision for the organization that includes needed core competencies, markets to be served, product mix, and resource needs. Secondly, it is a plan or high-level series of activities for realizing the future-state vision.

Processes – A process is a set of steps (or actions) that takes a set of inputs and produces an output. Process inputs consist of five main categories: methods, materials, equipment, people, and Mother Nature. The output from a process can be a product or service and can be either value-added, non-value-added, or some combination of both.

6.01: Lean Six Sigma: Culture, Strategy, and Processes ◄━━━━

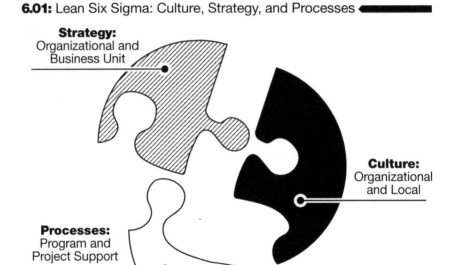

Strategy:
Organizational and Business Unit

Culture:
Organizational and Local

Processes:
Program and Project Support

We need to consider elements of culture, strategy, and processes for any organizational initiative, including Lean Six Sigma. Unfortunately, many organizations implement Lean Six Sigma without considering, let alone addressing, these three elements. If leadership is to successfully implement a Lean Six Sigma program, it needs to understand and address all three of these critical elements. If leaders don't ensure that all three elements are addressed, the elements will not be aligned, with the result that figure 6.01 depicts.

The key for leadership is to ensure that these three elements are integrated as shown below. By harmonizing the culture, strategy, and processes, the organization becomes aligned and performance is enhanced. The result is a Lean Six Sigma program that reaches its full potential.

6.02: Lean Six Sigma: An Integrated Model

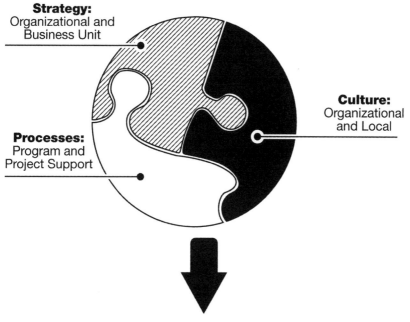

Operational Excellence

The problem with most Lean Six Sigma implementations is that leaders do not address the areas of strategy or culture. The propensity is to invest in providing Black Belts and Green Belts with the necessary skills, but to fail to address the issues of how the organizational culture and organizational strategy will interact and align with the use of Lean Six Sigma.

The most difficult thing to align is culture, as it has a high level of inertia; it takes a tremendous amount of force to begin shifting it. However, it is also the most important thing to address since it will override both strategy and process. Culture is analogous to an iceberg. Most of the iceberg is below the waterline and cannot be seen. Culture is the same way. A part of it is explicit and can be readily seen, but much of it is implicit and cannot be readily seen. Rather, immersion in the organization is required to identify the implicit part of the culture. And like an iceberg, culture is difficult, but not impossible, to move. Icebergs are moved by large oceangoing tugboats. When they first begin to tow the iceberg, the movement is imperceptible due to the huge inertia contained in an iceberg. However, over time, the iceberg begins to move and slowly it picks up speed. It is the same with culture. If leadership begins to push on the culture with a strong and consistent force, it will slowly begin to change.

6.03: Culture: The Dominant Factor

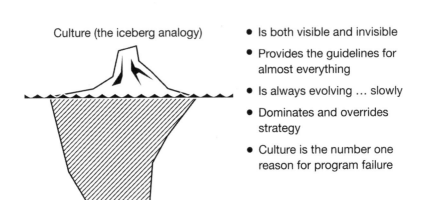

Culture (the iceberg analogy)

- Is both visible and invisible
- Provides the guidelines for almost everything
- Is always evolving ... slowly
- Dominates and overrides strategy
- Culture is the number one reason for program failure

If the leadership successfully integrates culture, strategy, and processes, the organization will be aligned, focused, and effective. Everyone will be pulling in the same direction with the knowledge and skills necessary to drive the organization forward and allow it to achieve its leaders' strategic vision. The Lean Six Sigma Deployment Roadmap is designed to ensure that the leadership is addressing all three of the key elements in a way that will ensure Lean Six Sigma success.

DEPLOYMENT ROADMAP OVERVIEW

Each of the seven phases of the Deployment Roadmap, shown in figure 6.04, contains a set of activities that the organization needs to undertake to ensure Lean Six Sigma success. These actions cover culture-, strategy-, and process-related needs. Each of these phases builds upon the activities of the previous phases. The key to success is to not shortcut the process of building a successful and sustainable program. The tendency of many organizations is to try to leap directly to generating improvement without setting in place the processes and systems to ensure success. Jumping directly to training and projects may generate some success, but the efforts exerted by the teams to show improvement will have to be far greater, they will encounter additional barriers, and their resources will be further constrained. Even more disconcerting is that if the organization does not put in place and use such elements as a robust project selection method, it is highly likely that it will select the wrong projects. This can mean that any success at a project level may not translate into organizational improvement. In these cases, it is also highly unlikely that the limited success achieved will be sustainable.

6.04: Seven-Phase Lean Six Sigma Deployment Roadmap

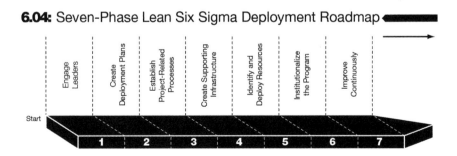

THE SEVEN-PHASE LEAN SIX SIGMA DEPLOYMENT ROADMAP

Brief descriptions of the seven phases of Lean Six Sigma deployment follow:

Engage leaders – This first phase centers on activities that ensure the leadership has a unified vision for the Lean Six Sigma program and its implementation. The team undertakes high-level activities such as setting defined goals for the initiative and establishing overall resource requirements. An outside consultant with experience in Lean Six Sigma implementation typically leads the activities in this first phase.

Create deployment plans – After aligning leadership, the external consultant works with the organization's leaders to identify deployment team personnel. Once the organization identifies these people, it defines their responsibilities and the deployment teams create detailed deployment plans. The leaders assess the organizational culture, and the team factors the assessment results into the deployment planning process.

Establish project-related processes – The organization establishes key project-related processes, including project selection and project tracking, to ensure that the initiative focuses on what is important to leadership and that it can compute the return on investment for the program.

Create supporting infrastructure – Determinations as to the necessary IT structures are a key aspect of this phase. Additionally, the organization must consider other issues such as knowledge management and the creation of a comprehensive communication plan to create pull for Lean Six Sigma within the organization.

Identify and deploy resources – In this phase, the organization identifies Black Belts and Green Belts, assigns their projects, and trains them. The project teams commence process-improvement activities and business results begin to be delivered.

Institutionalize the program – If Lean Six Sigma is to be part of the organizational fabric, it must be integrated into the existing organizational structures and not be seen as a separate entity. This phase entails activities to ensure that Lean Six Sigma is integrated into existing HR, Operations, Sales, Information Technology, Finance, and other functional structures.

Improve continuously – A well-run Lean Six Sigma program "eats its own cooking." That is, the Lean Six Sigma program itself must practice disciplined, continuous improvement. This is done through the ongoing assessment of key program metrics as well as development of human assets and supporting infrastructure.

DETAILED CHECKLISTS

Supporting the roadmap is a series of checklists, one for each phase in the deployment process. The checklists consist of a series of things that may need addressing as part of ensuring that the deployment team and leadership have considered and acted on all appropriate issues in each phase. Leadership and the deployment team, as appropriate, review the checklists. They review each item to determine if it is applicable to the organization and, if so, what action, if any, they need to take.

We have designed the checklists to cover all necessary issues regardless of the size of business or the organization. As the checklists are reviewed, it will become apparent that not every item applies to every organization. Likewise, many of the applicable items may have been previously addressed in the course of business so that no additional activity is required. The key in using the checklists is to find any and all holes in the framework for success and get the holes filled before they become hazardous to Lean Six Sigma success.

It is not necessary that every item within a phase be completed before moving on to the next phase in the deployment process. Some of the action items necessary for Lean Six Sigma success have significant lead times, which means that full implementation of these items may require a period of time. It is fully appropriate to move forward into subsequent phases before completing such tasks. However, it is required that there be a plan in place to responsibly deal with these longer-lead-time items, including a scheduled completion date and the assignment of responsibility to a specific individual. The deployment team will then be responsible for tracking progress on these long-lead-time items as the team proceeds through the Deployment Roadmap. For tasks that are short term in duration, the methodology requires that deployment teams will complete those tasks prior to moving on to the next phase of the Lean Six Sigma Deployment Roadmap.

If leadership follows the Deployment Roadmap, it will ensure that the organization is aligned and there is a supporting infrastructure for the Lean Six Sigma efforts. Projects will be well chosen, properly resourced, and successful in generating business results. The team will compile Lean Six Sigma gains and determine the performance of the continuous-improvement effort, as well as the return on the organization's investment. Additionally, the program will be sustainable and, with time, become part of the organization's way of doing business.

LEADERSHIP INVOLVEMENT

A disengaged leadership team that delegates continuous improvement to others and shuns involvement will oversee program failure. For the Lean Six Sigma initiative to be successful, it is necessary for senior leadership to be actively engaged. Engaged means not just the less visible activities of providing resources, etc., but the proactive, visible advocacy for the initiative. In initiating such a program, leadership does not get to sign a check and walk away. This is not to suggest that senior leaders need to devote the majority of their time to the Lean Six Sigma initiative. It is not as much the quantity of time dedicated to Lean Six Sigma support, as it is the quality of the activities. This is an area where the roadmap can provide significant value to the organization's leaders through the selection of high value-added activities. The roadmap spells out specific activities to be undertaken by senior leaders and other managers. This way, time spent supporting the initiative will be optimized, allowing leaders to provide high levels of support without having to dedicate a high proportion of their time.

Advocacy versus Involvement

When we talk about leadership involvement in the initiative, we're speaking of advocacy and commitment, not passive acquiescence. "Going through the motions" is not going to generate success and begin to change the way the organization operates; rather, advocacy is needed. Management needs to be committed to both the long-term and short-term success of the continuous-improvement effort. Examples of commitment and advocacy include a visible commitment of resources, public support of Lean Six Sigma efforts, and holding managers accountable. It is through commitment and advocacy that success will be obtained.

SHORTCUTTING THE PROCESS

It is essential that the organization not shortcut the deployment process. A "ready, fire, aim" mentality will not lead to success, but only to frustration. For example, there is no sense in attempting to determine resource requirements until leadership has an aligned vision for what the program is to accomplish. Likewise, there is no sense in working on projects and doing training before a robust project selection process is understood and established. There is a reason the Deployment Roadmap is laid out the way it is. There is a logical sequence of phases, each of which builds upon the others before it.

LONG-TERM EVOLUTION

In the short term, the objective of the organization is to implement and sustain a Lean Six Sigma program. However, the long-term goal is not to have a Lean Six Sigma program, but rather to have

Lean Six Sigma become part of the way the organization does business. It is this evolution from being a separate and distinct program to becoming part of the organizational fabric and culture that is the true hallmark of success. The Lean Six Sigma Deployment Roadmap is designed to lay the foundation for this transition to occur. Failure to lay the proper foundation will at best delay and at worst prevent this evolution in the way the organization operates.

The Lean Six Sigma Deployment Roadmap identifies for the leadership not only the activities that need to take place to successfully implement in the short run, but also the things that need to become part of the organizational fabric to ensure long-term success.

CONTINUOUS-IMPROVEMENT MATURITY

If one looks at the maturity of the organization in terms of continuous improvement, there is a clear progression that begins with treating continuous improvement as an unneeded luxury to ultimately embracing it as part of the culture. Figure 6.05 illustrates this maturation.

When the organization first engages with the idea of continuous improvement, it tends to be perceived as a luxury. It is not truly adopted by the organization or the management of the organization. It is supported only by ad hoc activity. As a result, it is often focused on the wrong activities and delivers, at best, sporadic results. Organizations that take this approach are often described as "firefighting" organizations. That is, they run from crisis to crisis using seemingly random, unstructured tools and techniques in response to product problems.

As the effort matures it begins to become defined. However, management support is minimal, resulting in a continuous-improvement effort that is starved for resources and does not have a robust support structure. Continuous improvement is no longer seen as a luxury, but is viewed as something that is desired across the organization, even if it does not yet exist. At this point, the organization will still be getting ad hoc or marginal results.

Further maturation results in a continuous-improvement program that is not only defined but is well managed. At this stage, management is fully supportive of the continuous-improvement efforts and there is a robust and cohesive continuous-improvement organization. This structure ensures efforts are focused on key business goals and objectives. A structured method for the use of continuous-improvement tools exists and the program is generating meaningful benefit to the organization. Continuous improvement at this stage of maturity generates a small to moderate competitive advantage to the organization.

Continuing further through the maturation process, management not only supports continuous improvement, it fully understands and embraces it. It is at this point that such efforts are viewed as essential to organizational competitiveness and to organizational success. Process improvements are no longer the sole province of a dedicated function within the organization, but, rather, pervade the organization as a whole and have become a part of the culture. The formal continuous-improvement organization now has the primary function of being a catalyst for enhancing the speed and effectiveness of others' efforts rather than undertaking efforts themselves. Tools and methods to drive process improvement are structured and standardized throughout the organization. Furthermore the organization is utilizing tools such as knowledge management to speed the effort. It is at this point that continuous improvement begins to become a true competitive advantage to the organization.

Finally, the last step in the maturation process is the evolution from a program to a way of doing business; it is a part of the culture. At this stage, continuous improvement has become woven into the organizational fabric from the very top of the organization to the very bottom. Management is now fully engaged in continuous improvement as part of its daily activities, as are all other employees. Throughout the organization, continuous-improvement efforts exist every day as part of the nature of the company. Organizational thinking has shifted from short-term to long-term and is focused on value streams and systems. Short-term thinking and focusing on functions or segments of the value stream no longer exist. All organizational structures—whether they be reward systems, IT systems, and other support structures—fully embrace and support the continuous-improvement process. The continuous-improvement efforts in this stage of maturity enable world-class performance in terms of quality, cost, and customer satisfaction.

6.05: Lean Six Sigma Maturity Model ◄━━━━━━━━━━━━━━

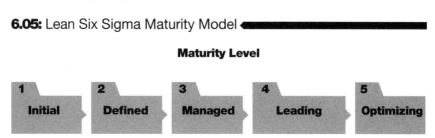

The next seven chapters will cover the seven phases of the Deployment Roadmap in detail.

Go to www.e-mri.net/roadmap.htm to download a free, full-color, 24" x 36" or 11" x 17" PDF of the eMRI Lean Six Sigma Deployment Roadmap.

CHAPTER 7

ENGAGE LEADERS

In successful Lean Six Sigma engagements, senior leadership provides the strategic vision while the business units provide the tactical-level decisions to ensure that the strategic vision is realized. It is in this **first** of the seven phases of the Lean Six Sigma Deployment Roadmap that senior leadership will create and communicate the strategic vision for the Lean Six Sigma program and begin to prepare the organization for its implementation.

Since leaders are most often not experts in continuous improvement, they usually hire a consultant or other outside resource to facilitate the activities surrounding the implementation of Lean Six Sigma. As the organization proceeds through the implementation process, a deployment Champion and a deployment team take responsibility for managing the Lean Six Sigma implementation. The consultant then works with the deployment Champion and team to undertake deployment activities. Through training and consultation, the eventual goal is that the organization becomes self-sufficient in running the Lean Six Sigma program.

The first phase of the Deployment Roadmap consists of the following activities:

CULTURE-RELATED ACTIVITIES

There are two culture-related activities: cultural assessment and assessing cultural imperatives.

7.01: Engage Leaders ◄━━━━━━━━━━━━━━━━━━━━━━

> **Engage Leaders**
>
> *Culture*
> • Conduct preliminary cultural assessment
> • Identify key cultural imperatives
>
> *Strategy*
> • Align on the vision for continuous improvement
> • Establish Lean Six Sigma goals and objectives
> • Conduct a readiness gap assessment
> • Identify corporate and business unit Champions
> • Create a high-level organizational deployment plan
> • Assess resource requirements

Conduct Preliminary Cultural Assessment

In this first phase, the organization begins the process of performing a cultural assessment. The cultural assessment provides the leadership, and those tasked with implementing the program, with extremely valuable information about how culture will enable or inhibit the implementation effort. This in turn provides guidance on how to tailor the implementation to deal with significant cultural issues.

A co-worker of mine has expressed the value of a cultural assessment as follows: Imagine you are standing at the entrance to a large room. The room is pitch black and full of obstacles and trip hazards. Somewhere on the other side of the room is a door that is the exit. Your task is to get to the exit. Most people will eventually achieve their goal and get to the other door. However, in the process of getting to the exit, they will bump into obstacles and trip and fall. By the time they get to the opposite door, they will be bloodied and bruised. They also will have taken a long time to get there. Performing a cultural assessment is the equivalent of turning on the lights. The obstacles to achieving the goal have not gone away, but they are now visible. You will still have to plan a way to circumvent the obstacles, but that is a lot easier if you know what and where they are. Performing the assessment does not remove any of the barriers or alter the culture. Rather, it shines a light on both the supporting aspects and inhibiting aspects of the organization's culture as it relates to the successful implementation of Lean Six Sigma.

The importance of a cultural assessment is increased by the fact that culture is not uniform in an organization. The culture in one department may be quite different from that in another. Even within a department, there can be cultural variations from location to location. The result of these varied cultures is that what may be an effective strategy for implementation in a sales organization, for example, may actually hinder acceptance in manufacturing. For this reason, cultural assessments can be of tremendous value in assisting the deployment Champions, not only in effectively launching the program, but also in sustaining it.

In this phase of the implementation, we recommend that you limit the cultural assessment to the executive level of the organization. Typically, the assessment is relatively painless to administer and one handles it through an online survey or similar instrument. You convey the findings of the assessment to the leadership team. This allows the team to better understand the cultural strengths that will be supportive of Lean Six Sigma, and also the aspects of the culture that will not be supportive or even might potentially inhibit successful implementation and sustainment. The point of the assessment is not to determine if the culture is good or bad; there is no judgment to be made. Rather, one wants to turn on the proverbial light in the room so the leaders have a clear view, they understand the cultural challenges, and chart the proper course.

Identify Key Cultural Imperatives

Cultural imperatives are actions that you need to undertake to address key aspects of the organizational culture as it relates to Lean Six Sigma.

While the result of the leadership-level cultural assessment is unique to each organization, it normally identifies several key cultural imperatives. Whether these cultural imperatives are many or few, they provide leadership with a set of key considerations that require action to ensure the team successfully implements and sustains the Lean Six Sigma program.

Entire organizations often have specific cultures. For example, governmental and military organizations often have a culture that values control and command. Such a culture is very systems oriented, which has its strengths (stability and a structured process focus), but also has its weaknesses (difficulty in making rapid change or adapting to unusual situations). An example of very different culture is a technology start-up. This kind of organization normally is flexible and has an external customer focus. Organizational strengths include the ability to adapt and change rapidly as well as a strong external customer focus, while weaknesses include a lack of process focus and stability. Neither of the cultures noted is good or bad. These examples merely serve to illustrate that every culture is unique and the deployment team must assess it to determine if specific activities are needed to address some of the cultural weaknesses that might affect the implementation of Lean Six Sigma.

Just as organizations can have unique cultures, different departments or functions within the organization can also have different cultural characteristics. These characteristics may be favorable toward the deployment of Lean Six Sigma or they could be challenges to successful implementation. For example, the accounting and quality assurance functions tend to be very control-and-command oriented, with strict adherence to process and stability, and they tend to be inward looking. This contrasts with the culture of the sales organization. It tends to be flexible and adaptable, focused heavily on the customer, and chafes at the presence of process restrictions that inhibit flexibility and the ability to make decisions on the fly to address customer needs.

In viewing the above example, it should be noted that in both cases the cultural characteristics noted are all positive, given the responsibilities of the function. It is highly desirable to have the accounting and quality functions stable and process based. Having an accounting or quality assurance function that "flies by the seat of its pants" or makes up rules as it goes is not comforting to anyone. Likewise, a sales function that cannot focus externally on the customer and advocate a flexible approach to meeting customer needs is distressing as well. In fact, to perform at a high level, different functions need to have different cultural characteristics.

Organizational leaders will tend to reflect the cultural traits of the functions they manage. The cultural assessment will likely reveal these differences among leaders. The implication is that different leaders will have different views regarding the adaptation of Lean Six Sigma, as well as face different challenges in implementation. Because Lean Six Sigma is a structured methodology, it is often viewed by the more creative and flexible functions, such as product development and sales, as a restrictive methodology that chokes off creativity and innovation. The goal of Lean Six Sigma, of course, is not to stifle creativity, but rather to make creative functions more efficient and value-added. For example, Lean Six Sigma could be applied to product development. It could enhance the use of data to drive decision making, to determine which potential products or services should proceed to the next step in development and which should be terminated. In sales, Lean Six Sigma could be used to pull non-value-added steps and activity out of the sales processes, allowing more time to be spent actually selling to customers.

By assessing the culture and identifying cultural imperatives, the leadership is laying a strong foundation for the implementation of Lean Six Sigma.

STRATEGY-RELATED ACTIVITIES

Align on the Vision for Continuous Improvement

The first strategic step in this phase is aligning the senior leadership team's vision for continuous improvement. The vision statement captures leadership's long-term view of what the continuous-improvement effort will look like and what it will do for the organization with respect to increasing value, affecting competitive position, and delivering business results. If the organization's leaders are not aligned on this vision, successful implementation is unlikely. A unified vision is necessary to accurately determine what the Lean Six Sigma initiative will be tasked to accomplish, how success will be judged, who needs to be involved, etc. All the other decisions and judgments about implementing, operating, and sustaining the Lean Six Sigma initiative depend on the shared, unified vision which leadership has for continuous improvement.

Establish Lean Six Sigma Goals and Objectives

Once the vision for continuous improvement has been established, high-level organizational goals for the initiative are set. If the vision has been well crafted, leadership will be able to develop a comprehensive set of goals that provides clear direction for those tasked with leading the continuous-improvement effort.

A good set of goals has both an internal and external (customer) focus. While an incentive for many organizations is cost reduction, you can also use Lean Six Sigma to accomplish a much wider range of goals than just saving money. For example, are there external, customer-focused outcomes you desire of the initiative? If so, you need to identify these goals in this phase so that as the initiative is rolled out, those you charge with ensuring success have clear targets. You can use Lean Six Sigma to increase customer loyalty and repeat purchases, shorten service-cycle times, enhance your organization's ability to offer new products and services, or improve product and service quality.

There are other types of less obvious goals to consider as well. One organization considering Lean Six Sigma had grown through the acquisition of many smaller companies. However, the organization had not done a robust job of integrating the acquisitions. As a result, much non-value-added activity was taking place due to redundant activity, lack of communication between the business units, etc. To improve performance, leadership stated that a key goal of the Lean Six Sigma program was to improve the integration of the company's business units.

Because the goal was explicitly identified up front, those charged with deployment were able to ensure that the team properly prioritized projects related to improved integration.

The organization should also consider whether there are cultural goals for the effort. That is, does leadership want Lean Six Sigma to be a part of creating a shift in culture? A senior manager with whom we had worked in implementing Lean Six Sigma provided a good example of a cultural transformation delivered by the program. He literally stated that he didn't care if his organization ever did another successful Lean Six Sigma project because something much more important had happened within his organization.

"In the past," he stated, "everyone was driven by opinion. Today, because of Lean Six Sigma, everything we do is data driven. For example, if you tell someone, anyone, that there is going to be a meeting, the first words out of their mouth will be, 'Who's bringing the data?' Everyone in the company, regardless of rank or department, now thinks the same way." He fully credited Lean Six Sigma for transforming the culture in a way that had profound implications for the organization and its performance.

Another part of establishing goals is determining the initial scope of the Lean Six Sigma program. For example, larger organizations may choose to pilot Lean Six Sigma within a certain segment of their operations. Such segmentation could take place by geographic location, function, market segment, etc. For a larger organization, this segmentation allows resources to be more highly focused on a subset of the organization, increasing the probability of Lean Six Sigma success. It may also afford the organization an opportunity to learn what factors come into play in supporting or inhibiting success. This knowledge can then be used when launching Lean Six Sigma across the rest of the organization, ensuring an even more effective use of resources.

A final consideration to make when establishing goals and objectives is to determine how to characterize financial results. That is, from the finance and accounting perspective, how will you calculate the financial impact of a project? Here, in the first phase of the Deployment Roadmap, it is wise to begin a philosophical discussion as to what the scope of this task will actually be. Will the organization attempt to financially characterize things such as customer satisfaction or will the organization accept that increased customer satisfaction is of benefit to the organization and no financial characterization is necessary?

Conduct a Readiness Gap Assessment

One of the tasks that you must undertake to successfully deploy Lean Six Sigma is to determine the gap between the current state and the required future state that will enable you to successfully implement and sustain the program. The gap analysis will primarily look at two things. First, the consultant reviews the history of continuous-improvement activities within the organization, along with the current level of maturity and level of sophistication and effectiveness. Second, the consultant reviews the organization to determine which of the processes and systems that are required to successfully implement and sustain the program are currently in place, as well as reviews the robustness of those same processes and systems. The consultant does this, among other things, by comparing the current state to the Deployment Roadmap checklists I mentioned in chapter 6. The result of the gap analysis is a report that delineates the gaps you need to fill to successfully implement and sustain Lean Six Sigma.

Identify Corporate and Business Unit Champions

It is in this phase that you need to identify the organizational Champion and business unit Champions. The quality, depth, and breadth of the skill sets of the people assigned to deployment activities is more important than the quantity of resources assigned. It is important that these people be selected carefully. We recommend that the organizational Champion report directly to the senior executive in the organization. The Champion should be someone who is both well respected in the organization and has the proper skills, as this is the person who will lead the remainder of the implementation effort. He or she will need to have strong planning and project management skills as well as excellent communication skills.

In larger organizations, we recommend that each business unit identify a Lean Six Sigma deployment Champion as well. These individuals will work with the organizational Champion to coordinate and oversee the implementation of the initiative. As with the organization-wide Champion, it is important that you select the business unit Champions based on their skills. These deployment Champions will be responsible for laying the foundation that allows Lean Six Sigma projects to be successfully completed.

7.02: Program Structure

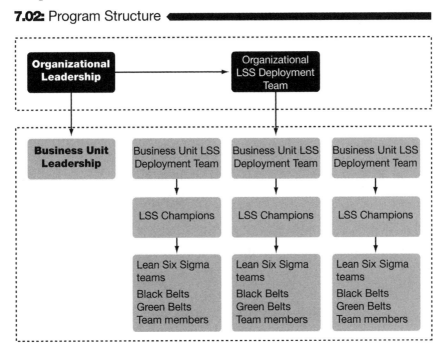

Deployment Champions do not work in isolation, but rather are supported by deployment teams. The team's exact composition is determined case by case. There are several things to keep in mind when selecting personnel to support the deployment Champion as part of the team. It is extremely desirable to have a highly cross-functional deployment team that cuts across as many of the organization's functional areas as possible. It is also desirable to have a multilevel team; that is, the team should contain members from multiple levels within the organization. Different levels of the organization often have unique perspectives and these unique perspectives can be beneficial to successfully deploying Lean Six Sigma. Another factor to consider when selecting deployment team members is the level of influence the people have within the organization. This influence can be formal, which flows from rank or position, or it can be based on relationships, perceived expertise, etc.

Steering Committee

The other group that leadership needs to identify is the steering committee. The steering committee is not responsible for the initial deployment of Lean Six Sigma, but rather for managing the ongoing Lean Six Sigma program, evaluating its performance, charting its future direction, and making recommendations to the senior leadership team regarding the program.

It may very well be that the personnel that constitute the steering committee have a high degree of overlap with those on the deployment team. However, this is not necessarily the case. The personality, skills, and knowledge required to successfully deploy any new initiative in the organization are quite different from those necessary to successfully sustain and nurture it over a long period of time. So, it is likely that some members of the deployment team will not serve on the steering committee and vice versa.

Create a High-Level Organizational Deployment Plan

Before handing responsibility to the deployment Champion, leadership needs to lay out a high-level deployment plan, which the deployment Champion and the team will use to develop a detailed deployment plan. It will also later be rolled down to the business units so that high-level business unit deployment plans that support the organizational plan can be created.

This document is a high-level project plan identifying a limited number of critical tasks, milestones, and general timing. For example, the high-level plan might consist of milestones for each of the seven phases in the Deployment Roadmap. The deployment team will create the more detailed plan in the next phase.

Assess Resource Requirements

Once the goals for the program have been established, it is possible to begin defining the required resources. These resources include:

- people – program support, Black Belts, Green Belts, etc.;
- systems infrastructure (IT support); and
- other organizational support such as communications.

When identifying needs for resources, it is desirable to look ahead several years. For example, in larger organizations, there will almost certainly be the need for IT infrastructure to support Lean Six Sigma efforts. This infrastructure may be built or enhanced over a period of time. It would be extremely unfortunate if the organization made a large investment of money, people, and other resources in year one, only to deprive the program of the resources necessary to sustain it longer term.

The resource that leaders most frequently underestimate is the time that the Black Belts and Green Belts will need to undertake their projects. Particularly, in challenging economic climates when resources are most scarce, most Lean Six Sigma Black Belts and Green Belts will have other functional responsibilities. While functional responsibilities and Lean Six Sigma activities are both important, managers tend to perceive functional responsibilities as more urgent. The result is that Lean Six Sigma activity is put on the back burner and projects wither and die. This will be discussed in more detail in chapter 11. It is important that leaders provide resources to the program so that individual areas do not become resource starved and Lean Six Sigma efforts yield little result.

The bottom line is that organizations get out of Lean Six Sigma what they put into it. If leadership provides adequate resources to the initiative relative to its goals, the initiative will be successful. If the initiative is resource starved relative to the goals, the results will be substandard.

ENGAGE LEADERS CHECKLIST

At the end of this chapter, and the next six chapters that describe the Deployment Roadmap in detail, is a checklist of questions (separated into the categories of culture, strategy, and process) that the deployment team should cover before proceeding to the next phase in the roadmap. For each question, the organization must determine whether the subject of the question is applicable. Larger organizations will find that most of the questions apply, while smaller organizations will find that only a subset applies. For every question that is applicable, the organization must then determine whether the subject, issue, or action covered by the question has been completed.

The list of applicable, not completed questions then forms the action item list for the deployment team. The action items can then be used to assemble a deployment plan where responsibilities, deadlines, etc., can be assigned to each action item. Note that while the team must complete some action items before it can responsibly move on to the next phase, it need not complete every action item in a phase before proceeding to the next. Whether or not you need to complete a given task before moving on to the next phase depends on the task and is up to the judgment of the Lean Six Sigma leadership and deployment team.

Engage Leaders Checklist ◀━━━━━━━━━━━

	Applicable?	Not Completed	Completed
Culture			
1. Has a leadership cultural assessment been completed?	☐	☐	☐
2. Has a leadership list of cultural issues been compiled?	☐	☐	☐
Strategy			
1. Has the senior executive endorsed the Lean Six Sigma program?	☐	☐	☐
2. Have the leaders developed a shared vision for continuous improvement?	☐	☐	☐
3. Have Lean Six Sigma program goals been established at the corporate level?	☐	☐	☐
4. Have Lean Six Sigma program goals been established at the business unit level?	☐	☐	☐
5. Do all Lean Six Sigma goals and objectives integrate with organizational goals?	☐	☐	☐
6. Has the voice of the customer been integrated into the program goals?	☐	☐	☐
7. Were the goal categories of finance, operations, customers, and employees considered?	☐	☐	☐
8. Will Lean Six Sigma be launched across the entire organization?	☐	☐	☐
9. Has a phased approach to the launch of Lean Six Sigma been developed?	☐	☐	☐
Process			
1. Has an executive Champion been appointed?	☐	☐	☐
2. Does the executive Champion report to the CEO?	☐	☐	☐
3. Have deployment Champions been identified?	☐	☐	☐

1 of 2 **Cont'd.** ▰▰▰▰▶

Engage Leaders Checklist ◄━━━━━━━━━━━━

	Applicable?	Not Completed	Completed

Process (Cont'd.)

4. Has the corporate executive team been scheduled for Lean Six Sigma leadership training? ☐ ☐ ☐

5. Has the business unit leadership been scheduled for Lean Six Sigma leadership training? ☐ ☐ ☐

6. Has leadership considered resource requirements in terms of people? ☐ ☐ ☐

7. Has leadership considered resource requirements for systems infrastructure? ☐ ☐ ☐

8. Has leadership considered resource requirements for management and leadership time? ☐ ☐ ☐

9. Has leadership made a multiyear funding commitment for the program? ☐ ☐ ☐

10. Has it been determined how projected project gains will be summed and reflected? ☐ ☐ ☐

11. Has a high-level corporate deployment plan been created? ☐ ☐ ☐

12. Does the deployment plan address program goals and objectives? ☐ ☐ ☐

13. Does the deployment plan address timing of actions and activities? ☐ ☐ ☐

14. Does the deployment plan address resource requirements? ☐ ☐ ☐

15. Does the deployment plan assign responsibility for each task? ☐ ☐ ☐

16. Does the deployment plan include a preliminary communication plan? ☐ ☐ ☐

17. Has the deployment plan addressed executive program review frequency? ☐ ☐ ☐

CHAPTER 8

CREATE DEPLOYMENT PLANS

In this **second** phase of the Lean Six Sigma Deployment Roadmap, the business units take the strategic vision communicated by organizational leadership and begin to lay out the tactical plans to accomplish it. If the overarching organization is to be successful, it is necessary that the organization itself, as well as the business units, have a plan in place to launch the initiative. It is also in this phase that leadership sets key inputs into the plans, such as business unit goals and objectives, and puts metrics into place to judge the performance of the continuous-improvement effort. Specific activities that will take place are shown in figure 8.01.

In the previous phase, leadership identified deployment Champions as the leaders of the Lean Six Sigma implementation. At the beginning of this phase, leadership identifies the other members of the deployment team. The team will support the Champion in ensuring a successful rollout. From this point forward, the deployment team undertakes or oversees virtually all of the activities I describe in this book. The size and makeup of the deployment teams is very much a function of organizational size, structure, culture, and other organizational attributes. Normally, the deployment Champions determine the members of the deployment teams in concert with leaders and an outside consultant who facilitates the rollout.

One of the first steps in this phase is to perform an organization-wide cultural assessment broken down by function and geographic location. This is a next step to the leadership cultural assessment discussed in the previous phase. The output of the cultural assessment provides the leadership of each business unit, department, and location with an understanding of the organization's strengths and weaknesses related to implementing and using Lean Six Sigma.

If a cultural assessment is not performed across the organization, the deployment team will not fully know and understand key information before implementing Lean Six Sigma. The likely result is that the organization's activities will not optimize the effectiveness of the Lean Six Sigma implementation. Again, we are back in the scenario where it is not the amount of resources that senior leadership supplies to the Lean Six Sigma effort, rather it is that the team cannot use those resources most effectively.

8.01: Create Deployment Plans ◄━━━━━━━━━━━━━━━

> ### Create Deployment Plans
>
> *Culture*
> - Conduct organization-wide cultural assessment
> - Identify key cultural imperatives
>
> *Strategy*
> - Provide leaders with deployment training
> - Establish business unit goals and objectives
> - Create deployment team charters
> - Refine organizational deployment plan
> - Create and align business unit plans
> - Establish metrics
>
> *Process*
> - Establish measurement systems
> - Provide Champion training

CULTURE-RELATED ACTIVITIES

Conduct Organization-Wide Cultural Assessment

In phase 1, the senior leadership undertook a cultural assessment to identify the culture or cultures that existed within the leadership ranks. As the deployment effort broadens, it will be beneficial to survey the organization as a whole to discern the variations in culture that exist between organizational business units, functional areas, and geographic locations. Again, it is possible, and in fact expected, that culture will vary across the organization. It is also likely that the cultural characteristics identified in various areas of the organization will not be fully aligned with the culture of the leadership team.

The leaders of each area of the organization will need to use the information that comes from the organization-wide cultural assessment to assist in the Lean Six Sigma deployment efforts. It is likely that the deployment teams will identify many different cultural elements in each area of the organization. While these elements will often overlap, it is probable that each area will have certain cultural aspects that are unique. By understanding the culture of each area within the organization, leadership can identify those cultural characteristics that are supportive of Lean Six Sigma and its deployment and those cultural characteristics that might inhibit the successful implementation of Lean Six Sigma.

Teams normally use survey instruments that they have third-party suppliers specifically design for the cultural assessment. Oftentimes, the instrument can be both distributed and analyzed online, minimizing the time and cost for the assessment.

Identify Key Cultural Imperatives

As a result of the cultural assessment, each function or location within the larger organization will have gained an understanding of its specific culture. Upon viewing the assessment, leaders will be able to identify the overarching, as well as the localized, challenges that each location or function will face to implement and then sustain Lean Six Sigma.

Historical events can create or influence localized cultural elements, or those elements could be related to other issues such as the function of the group, country, the region within a country, demographics of the staff, and type of business in which the organization engages. Certain past activities, especially those relating to continuous improvement, can affect the organizational culture and the organization's reaction to the Lean Six Sigma initiative. For example, if in the past the organization had a habit of jumping from program to program, this will create skepticism as to whether Lean Six Sigma is just the latest "flavor of the month." When this situation exists, people will be reluctant to commit resources to a program that does not (if past experience is a guide) have a long-term future. This scenario is seen most often when there are high rates of leadership turnover at the organizational or functional level.

Another example is when previous continuous-improvement programs have been poorly conceived or underresourced. In such situations, people will be skeptical of Lean Six Sigma and will seek to avoid or to minimize direct involvement in the program and the commitment of departmental resources.

One way to minimize some of these historical issues is to not call the program Lean Six Sigma. In fact, this is often a useful strategy even when there are not legacy issues that require consideration. Our group has launched Lean Six Sigma under several other names such as Advanced Problem Solving, The SMARTEN Program, Team Problem Solving, as well as calling it nothing more than Continuous Improvement Training. In each case, this renaming allowed the organization to characterize the initiative as the next logical step in the continuous-improvement journey.

For example, one organization previously launched a continuous-improvement initiative it called Problem Solving Skills. Rather than create the impression of jumping to another program (flavor of the month), the Lean Six Sigma initiative was renamed Advanced Problem Solving Skills, and the training materials and structures were then customized to align with the terminology taught in the original Problem Solving Skills training. Thus, leadership was credited with moving the continuous-improvement program forward and making it more robust while not "changing horses in midstream."

Other common cultural issues include:

- Rate-of-change issues
    - Resistance to change
    - Willingness to change, but only very slowly and methodically
    - Willingness to change, but only marginally, not significantly
    - Rush to change without planning
- Level-of-control issues
    - Micromanagement by leaders or managers
    - Disengaged leadership or management
    - General lack of process and structural controls
- Direction and diversity of focus issues
    - Internal focus on the function only (don't see the value stream or the customer)
    - Focus on the internal organization only (see the value stream, but not the external customer)
    - Customer-external focus excessive (no focus on process and the value stream)
- Process issues
    - Few processes or weak processes
    - Processes ignored or circumvented
    - Processes overly constraining
- Relationship issues
    - Preference for working alone, not in teams
    - Inability or unwillingness to work with other departments or functions
    - Need to include everyone in everything

The above issues are just some of the challenges that the organization may face as it embraces the Lean Six Sigma methodology. As you can see, some of the issues are diametrically opposed. You may see both diametrically opposed cultural elements in the same organization, in different functions or locations. This highlights the diversity of cultural challenges a Lean Six Sigma implementation faces.

Again, it is not a question of good or bad, it is a question of understanding what the cultural environment is so that it can be addressed during implementation.

STRATEGY-RELATED ACTIVITIES

The six strategy-related activities for this phase follow.

Provide Leaders with Deployment Training

Before the deployment Champions can begin the process of planning and executing a launch, they require training. The basis of the training is the Lean Six Sigma Deployment Roadmap. The training walks the deployment Champions and the teams through the steps they will need to undertake to successfully understand, implement, and deploy the program.

Typically, the classroom segment of deployment training takes a full day. The daylong session then serves as a springboard to further workshops associated with developing and executing the various components of the deployment plan.

Establish Business Unit Goals and Objectives

Each business unit needs to establish a set of weighted goals for the Lean Six Sigma initiative. Weighting the goals allows leadership to designate some goals as more important than others. In all cases, the business units should base their goals on the organizational goals and objectives from phase 1.

The business unit goals do not need to mimic the organization's goals, but they should support and integrate with them. Allowing each business unit to develop its own goals provides the business unit leaders with the input necessary to ensure that the implementation addresses their specific business imperatives. Without this flexibility, the program focuses on suboptimal objectives.

Create Deployment Team Charters

One of the tasks begun during the deployment training is the creation of team charters. Just as the Black Belt– and Green Belt–led teams use project charters, the Champions create deployment charters for the organization and the business units. The deployment charter specifies several things, including the goals and objectives of the continuous-improvement effort for the organization or business unit. It also identifies scope and key milestones associated with the deployment effort.

An explicit statement of the scope ensures that all team members are aligned on where Lean Six Sigma will be implemented. The milestones (project signposts indicating achievements of significance) are used to make big-picture judgments on implementation progress as well as serving as the starting point for detailed project planning.

In all cases, the charters are succinct documents to ensure that everybody on the team understands the key parameters surrounding the deployment effort.

Refine Organizational Deployment Plan

Like every project plan, the plan for Lean Six Sigma deployment is a living document. As circumstances change and events unfold, it is necessary to revisit the planning documents and make revisions. The business units use the organizational plan as a foundation for their work, so it is important that the organizational documents be current prior to dissemination for development of the business unit plans.

One factor that plays into the dynamic nature of the deployment plan is the knowledge gained by the leadership of the organization through leadership and deployment training and Champion training. As personnel become increasingly knowledgeable, they gain additional insights on how to best deploy Lean Six Sigma within the organization, and the updated deployment plan documents should reflect those insights.

Create and Align Business Unit Deployment Plans

Just as the organizational Champion needs to create a deployment planning document, each business unit also needs to complete a deployment plan. This document delineates the tasks the team needs to accomplish, the start date for each task, the end date for each task, and the person responsible for its completion. The team uses this plan to track actual progress versus plan (the baseline).

Establish Metrics

The organization must, early on, establish a coherent and integrated set of metrics to judge Lean Six Sigma success. The initial set will come from the organizational deployment team. The organizational metrics cascade down to the business units, whose deployment teams define the business unit metrics. It is essential that the business unit metrics support and integrate with those at the organizational level. The specific metrics the teams select depend on the goals and objectives that leadership established for the Lean Six Sigma program.

What does this mean to you? One common pitfall you often see in organizations is that they measure activity rather than success. For example, organizations often measure the number of people sent to Green Belt and Black Belt training. The number of people sent by the various departments or locations is perceived to be a measure of how well these portions of the business support the Lean Six Sigma effort. In fact, the correlation between the number of people sent to training classes and business success can be quite low.

One reason organizations often measure activity rather than results is that activity is often easier to measure. When determining what metrics to use to judge success, we recommend that the metrics you (or your teams) select correlate highly with business success. It is likely that when you determine these metrics, some of them may be difficult to measure. However, if these are the metrics that best correlate with business success, the organization must commit its resources to obtaining the data.

PROCESS-RELATED ACTIVITIES

There are two sets of process-related activities in this phase.

Establish Measurement Systems

Once the deployment teams have established the metrics, the next task is to determine how to measure them. As I noted before, measurement can often present challenges. It may be that IT solutions or IT support will be necessary to allow the organization to measure what is desired. This is why you should establish measurement systems this early in the Lean Six Sigma Deployment Roadmap.

Leaving the measurement systems until later creates one of two risks. First, the result may be that there is no objective, consistent method to judge success, and evaluations will be erroneous and variable. Second is the risk that if the organization waits until the last minute to create measurement systems, it will rush, shortcutting the development process, reverting to suboptimal metrics (e.g., activity) that are more easily measured.

Provide Champion Training

Champions are those responsible for selecting projects and providing resources for them (chapter 11 discusses their role in more detail). The training of Champions is roughly concurrent with providing deployment training for those on the deployment teams. Champion training provides a robust understanding of the conceptual framework for Lean Six Sigma as we described in chapters 1–4. It also includes a detailed understanding of project selection methodologies and how Champions properly support the Lean Six Sigma project teams.

When the leaders have established the business unit goals and objectives and the external consultant has conducted the Champion training, the Champions have the information and tools necessary to begin making sound Lean Six Sigma project decisions, using disciplined project selection methodologies.

Create Deployment Plans Checklist ◀

	Applicable?	Not Completed	Completed
Culture			
1. Has an organization-wide cultural assessment been undertaken?	☐	☐	☐
2. Has the response to the assessment been analyzed?	☐	☐	☐
3. Have leadership and management identified a set of actions necessary to bridge cultural gaps?	☐	☐	☐
Strategy			
1. Has the corporate and business unit leadership been trained?	☐	☐	☐
2. Has the high-level corporate deployment plan been reviewed or revised?	☐	☐	☐
3. Have business unit goals and objectives been established?	☐	☐	☐
4. Do business unit goals align with corporate goals?	☐	☐	☐
5. Have business unit deployment charters been created?	☐	☐	☐
6. Have business unit deployment plans been created?	☐	☐	☐
7. Do the deployment plans address program goals and objectives?	☐	☐	☐
8. Do the deployment plans address the timing of actions and activities?	☐	☐	☐
9. Do the deployment plans address resource requirements?	☐	☐	☐
10. Do the deployment plans assign responsibility for each task?	☐	☐	☐
11. Do the deployment plans include a preliminary communication plan?	☐	☐	☐

1 of 3 **Cont'd.** ▬▬▬▶

Create Deployment Plans Checklist ◄━━━━━━━

	Applicable?	Not Completed	Completed
Strategy (Cont'd.)			
12. Is the frequency of management reviews addressed in the deployment plan?	☐	☐	☐
13. Has an organizational risk assessment been performed?	☐	☐	☐
14. Have metrics been established to measure Lean Six Sigma program performance?	☐	☐	☐
Process			
1. Do measurement systems exist to capture the metrics data?	☐	☐	☐
2. Do the existing measurement systems measure with the necessary frequency?	☐	☐	☐
3. Do the existing measurement systems measure with the necessary sensitivity?	☐	☐	☐
4. Are plans in place to capture metrics not currently being measured?	☐	☐	☐
5. Has the effectiveness of all measurement systems been verified?	☐	☐	☐
6. How often will corporate and business unit deployment teams meet?	☐	☐	☐
7. Has a topical agenda for standard deployment team meetings been developed?	☐	☐	☐
8. Have required actions and behaviors been determined for all levels of management?	☐	☐	☐
9. Have the actions and behaviors been documented and reviewed by a subset of all levels of management?	☐	☐	☐
10. Have the agreed-upon behaviors been communicated to all pertinent management personnel?	☐	☐	☐

2 of 3 **Cont'd.** ■■■■━━►

Create Deployment Plans Checklist ◀━━━━━━━━━━━━

	Applicable?	Not Completed	Completed

Process (Cont'd.)

11. Have coaching and mentoring needs been identified? ☐ ☐ ☐

12. Have corresponding coaches and mentors been identified? ☐ ☐ ☐

13. Will Lean Six Sigma coaches and mentors be established for each level of management? ☐ ☐ ☐

14. Have the requirements for being a Lean Six Sigma coach been established? ☐ ☐ ☐

15. Has the minimum frequency of contact with coaches been established? ☐ ☐ ☐

16. Has a reporting structure for coaches been created such that tracking management actions and behaviors can take place? ☐ ☐ ☐

17. Has it been determined how instances of failure to adhere to required behaviors will be addressed? ☐ ☐ ☐

CHAPTER 9

ESTABLISH PROJECT-RELATED PROCESSES

This **third** phase of the Deployment Roadmap focuses on the process-related activities such as proper project selection and project tracking, necessary for project success.

The alignment and support of senior leadership along with robust deployment planning, while essential for Lean Six Sigma success, are not sufficient in and of themselves. The organization must also implement formal processes and structures to support the Lean Six Sigma project teams as they work through the DMAIC process to generate organizational improvement. Failing to provide such processes significantly increases the risk of project underperformance or failure.

The specific activities of this phase include:

9.01: Establish Project-Related Processes ◄▬▬▬▬▬▬

Establish Project-Related Processes

Strategy
- Establish how to financially characterize project results

Process
- Create and establish project selection processes
- Create and establish project tracking processes
- Create project summing and reporting processes
- Create and establish knowledge management processes
- Create a reward and recognition program

STRATEGY-RELATED ACTIVITIES

There is only one strategy-related activity in this phase.

Establish How to Financially Characterize Project Results

It is important that the organization establish how to compute financial results for projects. If this is not done early on in the deployment process, it can result in significant disagreement and conflict later. Left to their own devices, different business units and different departments will characterize the financial results of projects differently. This leaves the deployment Champions and the leadership of the organization attempting to judge performance by "comparing apples to oranges." It also leaves business units and functions in jeopardy of underperforming in the eyes of leadership, since they may view financial gains differently.

The key issue in financially characterizing projects is what the organization considers to be legitimate cost savings. Is it just going to be "hard" savings, or will "soft" savings be considered as well? For example, if a process is "leaned out" and the need for one-half of a full-time person is eliminated, does that count as a cost savings if it does not eliminate the position? Is the financial gain considered to be one-half of that person's annual cost to the organization? Or, are the savings the value of the other work that the person is able to undertake due to freeing up one-half of his or her time? Or, does the organization think that it has accrued no financial benefit because it has not lowered its overall cost structure?

For example, suppose a project "leans out" a process, resulting in eliminating inventory. This frees up working capital and floor space. Financial benefits include reducing the organization's need for capital, improving cash flow, reducing facility needs, and reducing the need for secondary services such as insurance. It also reduces movement, transportation, defects, and other forms of waste, resulting in further savings. How is the organization going to attempt to financially characterize all these benefits?

Another financial issue that the organization needs to consider is how, or even if, it will attempt to financially characterize other benefits such as improvements in customer satisfaction, which are challenging to quantify. This is not to say that it is necessary to try to financially quantify all of the above benefits. One organization we work with makes no attempt to financially quantify these types of benefits. It is the opinion of senior leadership that if managers or executives within the organization are not knowledgeable enough to understand the profound implication of these changes without financially quantifying them, they should not be working for the company. In essence, they differentiate themselves from the pack, of whom Dr. Deming once observed: "American companies are full of managers who know the cost of everything, and the value of nothing." Other organizations attempt to quantify as much as possible.

Organizations that try to describe every benefit financially often grossly underestimate the cost of poor quality (COPQ). COPQ is cost of expenditures for the prevention and detection of quality issues, plus the cost of internally experienced defects, plus the cost of having errors or defects reach customers. This is because COPQ is normally viewed and estimated using the accounting system. However, the accounting system is not designed to track the cost of poor quality.

While the accounting system can track some of the costs associated with poor quality—labor hours spent on inspection and audits, scrap and rework expenses, customer compensation due to quality problems, and expedited freight—it cannot comprehensively track the costs.

To illustrate, consider the minivan that my wife and I purchased many years ago. The vehicle was, to put it kindly, a disaster. For example, some of the things that failed on the vehicle included the door alarms randomly going on and off, the rear lift gate hinge breaking and the lift gate falling over, a broken tie rod, an intermittently nonworking audio system, a broken door striker, and inoperable door locks, just to name a few. While under warranty, the dealership made approximately $2,000 worth of repairs to the vehicle. After the warranty expired, we invested another $5,000 trying to keep it running.

One day, we were driving down the road, with our young daughter in the backseat. We were trying to determine how we were going to get the vehicle to the dealership for another repair. We were discussing our calendars when, suddenly, our daughter interrupted. My wife and I stopped our conversation and listened. What she said was: "Daddy, I'll never buy a _____ (and she said the name of the vehicle manufacturer)." Since that time, many years have passed and my daughter and my son are much older. All these years later, if you were to ask either of them today what kind of vehicle they wish to purchase, both of them, without hesitation, will inform you that they will never purchase a vehicle from that manufacturer.

If you were to ask the vehicle manufacturer to quantify the cost of poor quality associated with the vehicle I purchased, it would likely provide a number of $2,000 since that is what they invested in the vehicle while it was under warranty. A somewhat more enlightened perspective would put the cost of poor quality at approximately $7,000, what my wife and I invested in the vehicle as well as what the manufacturer paid under warranty. However, both of these numbers are a gross underestimation of the true cost of poor quality. The real cost is measured in lost sales. If we assume that the average person purchases seven vehicles over his or her lifetime, and the average price of that vehicle is $30,000, then my children's purchasing potential totals $420,000. In addition, my wife and I certainly never intend to purchase another vehicle from this manufacturer. At the time this took place we had a joint vehicle purchasing potential of six vehicles, worth another $180,000. That totals to $600,000 of business that will be given to other car manufacturers due to the poor quality of the vehicle.

The true cost of the poor quality of this one vehicle is not thousands or tens of thousands of dollars, but rather hundreds of thousands of dollars. Conservatively, the cost to the car manufacturer is a minimum of half a million dollars. Yet the accounting system will report the cost of poor quality as being only a few thousand dollars. Accounting systems are not designed to track the cost of poor quality.

Unfortunately, there is no way to accurately quantify the true cost of poor quality and the detrimental impact of poor quality on a company's financials. How many customers are lost due to poor product or service quality, and the value of those customers to the organization can never be proven. Most customers, upon experiencing poor service or product quality, just walk away. Nothing is ever communicated and the organization has no way to quantify the loss. Further compounding the difficulty in computing the cost of poor quality are issues such as the number of people that a dissatisfied customer communicates with about their experience and the effect of this communication.

Nonetheless, some academics, practitioners, and corporations have attempted to quantify the cost of poor quality as best they could. Published estimates of the cost of poor quality have ranged as high as 25 percent of an organization's revenue for poor performers and as low as 5 percent of the organization's revenue for top performers. Regardless of whether one believes that the cost of poor quality can range as high as 25 percent of an organization's revenue, it is abundantly clear that the cost is far greater than that tallied by the accounting system.

The cost of poor quality is directly related to the next task in the Deployment Roadmap, which is to create a project selection process. Frequently, when selecting projects, managers will state that the probable cost of solving a quality problem far outweighs the financial benefit and will seek to eliminate a project from consideration. To prove this point, they will look at the financial resources (e.g., capital expenditures) required to solve the problem and compare them to the cost of poor quality as measured by their accounting system. A similar phenomenon occurs in the Improve phase of the DMAIC process. Champions sometimes weight the cost of the Improve phase activities versus the cost of poor quality as measured by the accounting system. In either of these two situations, managers can easily make erroneous decisions because they do not properly understand the cost of poor quality, which was probably not computed comprehensively.

PROCESS-RELATED ACTIVITIES

There are three key project-related processes that the team must create and structure in this phase of the roadmap. They are shown graphically in figure 9.02:

9.02 Lean Six Sigma: Basic Structure

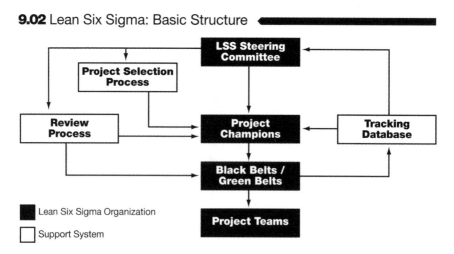

Create and Establish Project Selection Processes

A robust and standardized project selection process is imperative if the Lean Six Sigma program is to be successful. A failure to select the right projects can jeopardize the success of the entire Lean Six Sigma initiative, as figure 9.03 depicts.

The projects that the project Champions select must be projects that address key organizational strategies or goals. If they select projects that do not support the key goals and objectives of the organization, then even if the projects are successfully completed, the organization will not realize sufficient benefit. If the projects do not generate sufficient benefit to warrant the resources invested in them, having a Lean Six Sigma program does not make sense. Support for the program will dwindle and eventually the program will fail.

9.03: Wrong Project Selection

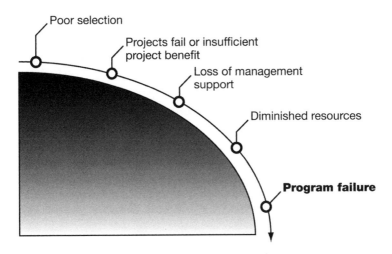

Poor selection

Projects fail or insufficient project benefit

Loss of management support

Diminished resources

Program failure

The establishment of the project selection process is, by necessity, a top-down process. It must start with the leadership and work its way down through the organization. It is imperative that the Lean Six Sigma teams work on issues and problems that are critical to the organization's success. This cannot be ensured unless leadership takes the time to articulate and document the key business imperatives when moving forward. Leadership is the group best qualified to identify the key goals and objectives on which the teams should focus. Once leadership has identified the key goals and objectives, Champions can ensure that the projects selected are supportive of the organizational goals. In this manner, the project teams' completion of the projects will result not only in project success, but also in organizational success. Figure 9.04 illustrates the top-down nature of the Lean Six Sigma deployment process. If activity begins with Black Belt and Green Belt training, the projects will not focus on the right things. Even if the projects are successful, they will not yield the desired business results.

As I mentioned in earlier chapters, organizations often make the mistake of leaping into the training of Black Belts and Green Belts without laying the necessary foundation for success. When this happens, they often select the wrong projects. Consequently, even if the projects are successful, they may not focus on the right things and may therefore not help the organization succeed.

There are several methodologies that Champions can use to drive the project selection process. The methodology that we normally use is a form of a prioritization matrix, along with a handful of filters to eliminate inappropriate projects. Several steps are involved in creating the project selection prioritization matrix.

9.04: The Lean Six Sigma Approach

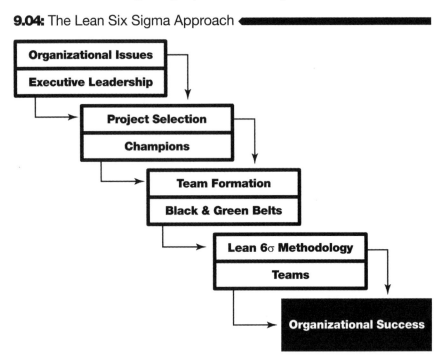

The first step is to work with leadership to determine the project selection criteria. This includes criteria that assess not only the anticipated benefits of the project, but also the risks associated with the project. Because the project selection criteria are based on what is most important to the organization, organizational and business unit leaders specify the criteria.

In terms of the project benefits, it is critical at this time to ensure that there is a balance between short-term and long-term thinking. Short-term thinking typically focuses on cost savings. Leadership teams tend to focus exclusively on short-term financial results when setting project selection criteria. While there is certainly a need for cost savings via reductions in non-value-added activity and improvements in quality, increased revenue is also needed. Over long periods of time, organizations cannot "cut their way to success." Longer-term success also comes from increasing revenue. Thus, leaders need to consider criteria focused on customers—such as improvements in customer loyalty and repeat purchases, improvements in product or service quality, or the ability to offer new products and services, etc.—as potential project selection criteria. Each organization must develop its own unique combination of project selection criteria.

It is also necessary to consider risk criteria. These are negative criteria that might cause an organization to not undertake a particular project. A few examples of project risk criteria include the expected duration of the project; total resource requirements; the need to use scarce resources; a potential increase in health, safety, or environmental risk; and the risk of interruption to operations.

Once the leaders have chosen the selection criteria, they weight the criteria. Not every criterion used to select the most desirable Lean Six Sigma projects is equally important. To differentiate the level of importance of the various criteria, leadership weights them, giving greater weight to those criteria that have the greatest importance.

It has been quite common, due to the economic dislocations of the past several years, to see organizations weighting cost savings more heavily than they have historically. In fact, the weighting of the project selection criteria needs to be revisited periodically by the steering committee to determine if alterations are required based on changes within the organization or its competitive environment. The economic turbulence of the last few years is an excellent example of why organizations must do this.

The next step is to develop a method for identifying potential projects. That is, a mechanism must be created that allows people to suggest potential projects for consideration. Project suggestions can come from anywhere in the organization. Some suggestions will come from senior leaders, some will come from management, and yet others will come from people out on the shop floor. It is desirable to gather project suggestions from as a broad a spectrum as possible.

Finally, the Champions score the potential projects against the criteria. There are various scoring systems that they can use to evaluate how well the potential projects meet the project selection criteria. We have found that relatively simple scoring systems work best in that they are more time efficient than more complex systems, yet still allow for adequate stratification of potential projects.

Selecting projects normally involves two main steps. First, the Champions use a quick and highly efficient screening methodology to separate the higher-potential projects from the lower-potential projects. At this point, the key is to not screen too heavily so as to erroneously eliminate a high-potential project.

Once the Champions have identified a pool of higher-potential projects, they use a second, more rigorous, project selection methodology. The more rigorous methodology involves the use of two project selection matrices: one focuses on project benefits and the other focuses on project risks. The Champions enter the project selection criteria, their weightings, and the potential projects into the matrices, and then score the potential projects against the criteria. Finally, the two matrices are integrated to form a graphical representation of project desirability. An example is shown in figure 9.05.

As you can see, the scaled reward runs along the horizontal axis and the scaled risk along the vertical axis. The scales are normalized with a maximum value of 10. The most desirable projects are those that fall in the lower right corner and the least desirable are those in the upper left corner. While figure 9.05 doesn't show this, the actual graphic is color coded into three zones of green, yellow, and red. This color-codes the projects into bands of relative desirability.

9.05: Project Selection Matrix

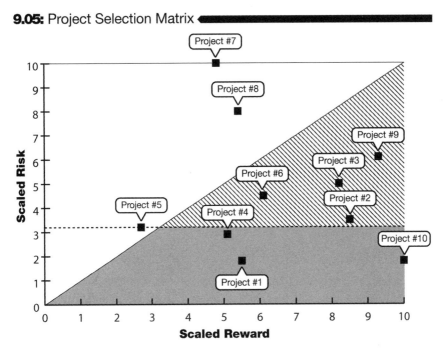

In the depiction above, the shaded area is the "green zone." The green zone is the zone where the projects are obvious winners in terms of project selection. The diagonally striped zone is the "yellow zone." The yellow zone is the zone where the project may well be viable, but the risk level is such that the organization should proceed with caution. The zone with no shading or diagonal striping is the "red zone." The red zone contains projects that appear to have more risk than potential benefit and don't make sense. The project selection template allows the organization to control the location of the lines separating the graph into green, yellow, and red zones. This allows each organization to independently and uniquely determine how it views reward and risk and what it considers to be a tolerable level of risk for a project. Risk-averse organizations can dial back the level of risk associated with being in the green or yellow zone. Organizations that are more aggressive can move in the other direction. In this way, each organization has the ability to customize the project selection process.

Voice of the Customer

The consideration of customer needs and wants is often referred to as the voice of the customer (VOC). Organizations need to directly solicit the VOC from all customers, i.e., both internal and external. There are several ways in which the organization can solicit the VOC, including focus groups, surveys, and analysis of data such as customer complaints. Not all methods are equal, as is shown in the graphic below.

9.06: Voice of the Customer

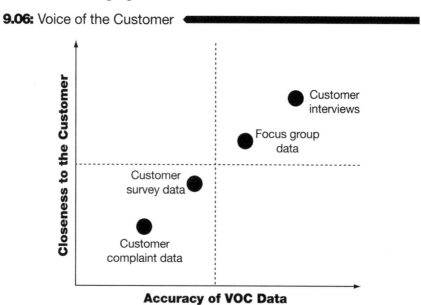

Unfortunately, the types of information most easily accessible, such as customer complaints, are also the least accurate and most distant from the customer. The good news is that many organizations already have significant amounts of VOC data. The challenge for the Lean Six Sigma deployment teams is accessing that information so that they can properly consider the voice of the customer when selecting projects.

It is also important to realize, when attempting to capture the voice of the customer, that the team must deliberately extract much of the information from the customer, who may not volunteer it. The Kano model best illustrates this phenomenon (see figure 9.07). In the Kano model, the vertical axis is the level of customer satisfaction. At the origin, the customer is neutral. Moving up the vertical axis, the customer becomes increasingly satisfied. Moving down, the customer becomes increasingly dissatisfied. The horizontal axis represents the degree to which the product or service has achieved a certain characteristic, feature, or function. The left side of the axis is 0 percent achievement and the right side is 100 percent achievement.

There are three types of features from the customer's perspective—basic, performance, and excitement. **Basic** features are those that the customer assumes will be there. That is, if the feature is not present and functional 100 percent of the time, the customer will be extremely dissatisfied. For example, if you purchase a car, you expect the car to start 100 percent of the time. If the car starts only 90 percent of the time, you will be extremely disappointed in the vehicle. Even when a basic feature, such as a vehicle starting, is present 100 percent of the time, the customer will merely be indifferent. However, anything less than 100 percent will result in high levels of dissatisfaction. **Performance** characteristics are those in which the more of it you get, the more satisfied you are. If you get very little, you are unhappy. If you get a moderate amount, you are ambivalent. However, if you get a lot of it, you are highly satisfied. A relevant example for most of us is fuel mileage. If you desire good fuel mileage, the higher it is, the more satisfied you are. If you're getting 15 miles to the gallon, you will be dissatisfied. At 25 miles per gallon, you might be ambivalent and at 35 miles per gallon you would be very satisfied. **Excitement** characteristics, or features, are those that the customer does not expect. Even if the customer does not get even a bit of it, he or she will not be dissatisfied. In other words, you don't miss what you never had. However, if the customer receives even a small amount of an excitement characteristic, he or she becomes very satisfied. For example, a certain brand of luxury vehicle can parallel-park itself. If you have never experienced this feature and you buy a car without it, you will not be dissatisfied with your car. However, if you get the feature, you will be very highly satisfied.

9.07: The Kano Model

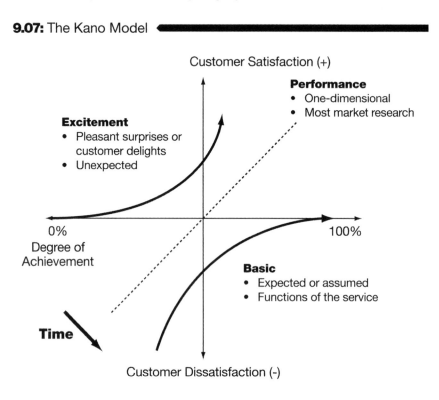

The Kano model shows that there are three types of characteristics, features, or functions associated with every product or service: basic, performance, and excitement.

Basic characteristics – Again, basic characteristics (features or functions) are ones that customers expect to be present 100 percent of the time. Note how the basic characteristics line rises as the feature approaches 100 percent attainment on the right side. At 100 percent attainment, the customer's perception has risen to one of indifference.

Performance characteristics – Performance characteristics (features or functions) are ones that customers hope to find, and are linear. The more of the characteristic there is, the higher the level of satisfaction.

Excitement characteristics – Excitement characteristics (features or functions) are also known as "delighters." They are most often things the customer does not even know that he or she wants. If the customer receives 0 percent of an excitement characteristic, they are indifferent. However, if they receive even a limited amount, their level of satisfaction quickly rises.

Time – Time causes excitement characteristics to devolve to performance characteristics and performance characteristics to devolve to basic characteristics, as customers' expectations change. An example of a current excitement characteristic would be auto-on wipers where, when moisture contacts the windshield, they automatically turn on. If this feature were not present, the customer would be indifferent. However, when they experience it for the first time, they will be delighted. Having said that, 20 years from now auto-on wipers will be a basic characteristic and every consumer will assume that the wipers will come on 100 percent of the time when moisture contacts the windshield.

The Kano model is useful because it illustrates an important point: Without deliberate probing, the customer will only volunteer information about one of the three types of characteristics—performance characteristics. The customer will not discuss basic characteristics because the customer assumes them. They will not discuss excitement characteristics because they don't know that they want them. The message is that passively listening to customers will only result in getting information about one of the three types of characteristics. If it wants to obtain a comprehensive understanding of the customer, the organization also needs to deliberately solicit information on the basic and excitement characteristics.

Create and Establish Project Tracking Processes

Just as important as selecting the right projects is making sure that the projects are rigorously tracked from beginning to end. A common failure is not to track the projects with rigor and standardization. If the Lean Six Sigma projects are not reviewed regularly, there is an increased risk that the projects will fall behind schedule or fail to fully meet their goals.

We recommend requiring that project teams pass through a series of tollgate reviews (many call them phase-exit reviews) done at the end of each phase of the DMAIC process. At the completion of each phase of the project, the team must present its documentation and the results for review by the Champion and a subset of the steering committee. The Champion and steering committee members allow the team to proceed to the next phase of the DMAIC process only if it has satisfactorily completed all required work in the phase under review. We also strongly recommend that executive leadership be a part of these tollgate reviews. That is not to say that every leader should attend every tollgate review. Rather, every senior leader should attend or participate in a predetermined number of tollgates per quarter.

It is in areas like project selection and project tracking that the use of technology comes into play. Larger organizations will need to put in place IT solutions that allow the organization to manage these tasks across a multitude of locations. Smaller organizations can get by with less costly and complex solutions. In chapter 10, "Create Supporting Infrastructure," I cover these types of issues in more detail.

Generally, a dashboard system works best for tracking projects. Projects are categorized as green, yellow, or red. Most typically, the dashboard monitors: (1) adherence to schedule and (2) achievement of project goals. Each of these two criteria is categorized as green, yellow, or red. Green projects are on or ahead of schedule and the projection is that they will meet the documented project closure date and achieve or exceed the desired project goals. Yellow projects are ones the evidence indicates are modestly behind schedule, have a project completion date at risk, or have a significant risk of not meeting their goals. Finally, red projects are substantially behind schedule, are highly unlikely to meet the scheduled project completion date, or are projected not to meet the project goals.

Too often, organizations leave the issue of project tracking until after projects are already under way. This almost inevitably results in projects falling behind schedule because schedule adherence is not visible. What is visible gets managed. If there is no or insufficient project tracking, there will be insufficient visibility of team performance.

Create Project Summing and Reporting Processes

From leadership's point of view, one of the most important systems to put in place is a process that sums the project gains. Without such a system, leadership cannot accurately determine whether the Lean Six Sigma program is meeting its goals and objectives and whether it is delivering sufficient return to justify ongoing support. On the flip side, if the program is delivering benefits substantially greater than those predicted and leadership cannot accurately determine this, then the lack of information may prevent them from applying increased resources to accelerate the program and increase the rate of continuous improvement.

Exactly how the team should sum and present project gains depends on the goals and objectives that leadership delineated for the program. Project results should be summed in a way that allows the leadership to compare the aggregated benefit of the projects to the goals set out for the program.

Whatever system is put in place, it will be necessary to be able to sum the gains at various levels throughout the organization to judge success, or lack thereof. For example, leadership needs to be able to look across the various business units within the organization and compare the performance of those business units. A business unit manager needs to be able to look across the various departments or functions within the business unit to determine the performance of the departments relative to each other. It may even be desirable or necessary to be able to look across multiple areas within a department.

Once again, the complexity of this task will be a function of the size of the organization. For large organizations, an IT solution will be necessary. The complexity of such a system will be a function of the complexity of the organization and the existence of or lack of structures already in place to support this activity.

Create and Establish Knowledge Management Processes

Knowledge management is the practice of identifying, collecting, storing, and disseminating knowledge. The larger the organization, the more important having a robust knowledge management process becomes. As an organization begins to undertake Lean Six Sigma, the number of Lean Six Sigma projects will begin to grow relatively rapidly. With each project will come knowledge. There needs to be a standardized method to collect, store, and disseminate this knowledge to others.

For example, a team in El Salvador has undertaken a project on an accounts payable process. Suppose that the result of the project is a substantial reduction in the amount of time and activity it takes to process each invoice. Concurrently, the team is able to reduce the number of mistakes or errors created in the process. If there is no knowledge management system in place, the learning that occurred as a part of this project will likely be lost. If a team in Finland decides to undertake a project on their accounts payable process which is similar to the one in El Salvador, they will end up "reinventing the wheel." If a team does not benefit from learning that took place on prior projects, the organization will be forced to expend significant resources unnecessarily.

The complexity of the knowledge management system is a function of the size and complexity of the organization. Small organizations may be able to get by with a folder on a shared drive on a server. Larger organizations with multiple locations need more sophisticated systems put in place. The stronger the knowledge management process is, the more efficient the use of organizational resources to complete future projects.

Create a Reward and Recognition Program

Participation on Lean Six Sigma teams requires a significant commitment on the part of all team members. It is important to recognize this commitment and contribution. One component of ensuring support for Lean Six Sigma is the creation of a reward and recognition program. Such a program can take many forms and comprise many things.

We recommend that you keep such programs simple and straightforward. Also, it is necessary that the reward and recognition system not create a separation between the Lean Six Sigma program and the rest of the organization. It is essential that as the reward and recognition program is developed, management does nothing to create the appearance that the Lean Six Sigma program and the people involved with it are separate or different from others within the organization.

We strongly recommend that the organization refrain from providing direct financial compensation to those who lead or participate on project teams. A Master Black Belt shared with me what might be the most egregious example of how **not** to structure a reward and recognition program. His employer actually paid Black Belts 10 percent of the first year's annual cost savings. No other member of the project teams received any compensation or recognition whatsoever. Furthermore, the corporation informed only the Black Belts about this compensation and deliberately did not convey this information to the rest of the organization at the onset of the Lean Six Sigma program.

After the completion of the first round of projects, checks were given out to the Black Belts that led the teams. Virtually instantaneously, the rest of the organization became aware of the compensation plan. To say that the compensation plan and the secrecy surrounding it caused a rift between Lean Six Sigma Black Belts and everyone else in the corporation would be an understatement. Almost immediately, the Black Belts became ostracized and completely isolated within the corporation. Project support from process experts became nonexistent. Within 12 months, the Lean Six Sigma program ceased to exist.

More desirable components of the reward and recognition program might include things such as:

- access to senior managers (Champions and others);
- peer recognition;
- enhanced long-term career advancement opportunities;
- insight into other areas of the organization;
- networking opportunities; and
- enhanced career skills.

There is no single optimal way to structure a reward and recognition program for a continuous-improvement program. However, whatever structure you arrive at will need aligning with the culture of the organization.

A good example of rewarding Lean Six Sigma project team personnel comes from a large multinational corporation with which we worked. The corporation set up a series of semiannual conferences focused on the sharing of best practices. Twice a year, the steering committee selected a limited number of Lean Six Sigma projects as best practices in the use of Lean Six Sigma tools or in the results that the projects generated. The two-day conferences were attended not only by the project teams but also by a group of the organization's most senior leaders. Over the course of two days, each of the teams presented to the senior leaders.

The primary benefit of these conferences, from the participants' point of view, was face time with senior leaders they otherwise would not have had. From the organization's point of view, not only were the best project teams being rewarded, but also the sharing of best practices across a global corporation allowed the company to accelerate the rate of change and improvement.

Establish Project-Related Processes Checklist ◀━━━━

	Applicable?	Not Completed	Completed
Project Selection Process			
1. Has responsibility for project selection been established?	☐	☐	☐
2. Have persons responsible for project selection been trained in the project selection process?	☐	☐	☐
3. Are there requisite (non-optional) criteria for project selection?	☐	☐	☐
4. Are the requisite criteria considerate of operational, design, and transactional process needs?	☐	☐	☐
5. Do the requisite criteria include both benefit and risk parameters?	☐	☐	☐
6. Has Finance been engaged in the creation of financial project metrics?	☐	☐	☐
7. How will the cost of poor quality be captured?	☐	☐	☐
8. Will both hard and soft savings be considered?	☐	☐	☐
9. Will costs not picked up by the accounting system be considered? If yes, how will they be measured or estimated?	☐	☐	☐
10. Are there criteria that will eliminate a project from consideration?	☐	☐	☐

1 of 5 **Cont'd.** ▬▬▬▶

Establish Project-Related Processes Checklist ◀━━━━━━

	Applicable?	Not Completed	Completed

Project Review Process

1. Will Champion reviews be required at a specified frequency? ☐ ☐ ☐

2. Has the frequency of Champion reviews been established? ☐ ☐ ☐

3. Has a formal agenda for individual project reviews been developed? ☐ ☐ ☐

4. How often will senior leadership (executive leadership and business unit leadership) participate in individual project reviews? ☐ ☐ ☐

5. Will continuous improvement personnel attend the leadership-level project reviews? ☐ ☐ ☐

6. Will phase-exit reviews be required at each phase of the DMAIC process? ☐ ☐ ☐

7. Has it been determined if phase-exit reviews will be separate from standard reviews or part of them? ☐ ☐ ☐

8. Has it been determined who will sign off on phase-exit reviews? ☐ ☐ ☐

9. Has a formal agenda been prepared for the phase-exit reviews? ☐ ☐ ☐

10. Will BBs be required to enter specific information into a project tracking system prior to or subsequent to the phase-exit review? ☐ ☐ ☐

11. If the use of specific Lean Six Sigma tools and methods is required for phase-exit, has a list of such tools been compiled? ☐ ☐ ☐

Project Queuing Process

1. How will top-down ideas for projects be captured and saved? ☐ ☐ ☐

2. How will bottom-up ideas for projects be captured and saved? ☐ ☐ ☐

2 of 5 **Cont'd.** ■■■■■■▶

Establish Project-Related Processes Checklist ◄━━━━━━

	Applicable?	Not Completed	Completed

Project Documentation

1. Has a standardized project format been developed with standardized forms? ☐ ☐ ☐

2. Have standardized formats for specific tools such as charters been developed? ☐ ☐ ☐

3. Will BBs be required to incorporate specific documents into every project notebook? ☐ ☐ ☐

4. Will BBs be required to use a specific subset of improvement tools on every project? ☐ ☐ ☐

5. Has it been determined what deliverables BBs will be required to upload to the corporate Lean Six Sigma database and with what frequency? ☐ ☐ ☐

6. Will a searchable database be created for knowledge management? ☐ ☐ ☐

7. If not, has it been established how access to the library of completed projects will be provided? ☐ ☐ ☐

8. Will the steering committee, Champions, and IT jointly decide the amount of functionality required in the knowledge management system? ☐ ☐ ☐

9. Have corporate sharing conferences been planned? ☐ ☐ ☐

10. Have business unit sharing conferences been planned? ☐ ☐ ☐

11. Will a journal of projects' abstracts be regularly prepared and distributed to all relevant personnel? ☐ ☐ ☐

12. Has it been determined how things gone right and things gone wrong will be captured and shared? ☐ ☐ ☐

13. Has it been determined how information overload and dumping will be prevented? ☐ ☐ ☐

3 of 5 **Cont'd.** ■■■■■■➤

Establish Project-Related Processes Checklist ◄━━━━━

	Applicable?	Not Completed	Completed
Project Documentation (Cont'd.)			
14. Has it been determined how deployment Champions will interface over time for purposes of sharing knowledge?	☐	☐	☐
15. Has it been determined how MBBs will interface over time for purposes of sharing knowledge?	☐	☐	☐
Project Closure			
1. Will Finance buy off on the financial gains for each project?	☐	☐	☐
2. Has it been established which Finance personnel will have this responsibility?	☐	☐	☐
3. Will there be a separate review meeting for project closure or will it be part of the regular review process?	☐	☐	☐
4. Has an agenda for closure meetings been developed?	☐	☐	☐
5. Will BBs be required to enter specific information into the project tracking system before or after project closure?	☐	☐	☐
Project Summing and Reporting			
1. Has leadership determined the information content and access that they desire on project gains?	☐	☐	☐
2. Have deployment Champions determined the information content and access that they desire on project gains?	☐	☐	☐
3. Has IT been engaged to assist in determining capabilities for summing gains and creating a set of management reports?	☐	☐	☐
4. Has Finance been engaged to assist in determining capabilities for summing gains and creating a set of management reports?	☐	☐	☐

4 of 5 **Cont'd.** ━━━━►

Establish Project-Related Processes Checklist ◄━━━━━

	Applicable?	Not Completed	Completed

Project Summing and Reporting (Cont'd.)

	Applicable?	Not Completed	Completed
5. Has it been determined who will have access to each summary report on project gains?	☐	☐	☐
6. Will a project gains report be developed for universal access?	☐	☐	☐
7. Will the continuous improvement function have a meeting schedule for reporting to leadership?	☐	☐	☐
8. Have attendance and frequency of such meetings been determined?	☐	☐	☐

Reward and Recognition

	Applicable?	Not Completed	Completed
1. Will there be a formal reward and recognition program?	☐	☐	☐
2. Have eligibility requirements been established?	☐	☐	☐
3. Have specific rewards and recognition been identified?	☐	☐	☐

5 of 5

CHAPTER 10

CREATE SUPPORTING INFRASTRUCTURE

In this **fourth** phase of the Deployment Roadmap, the organization continues to lay the groundwork for ensuring that Lean Six Sigma becomes part of the organization's way of doing business. It is to the organization's advantage that the continuous-improvement program evolves from a program to the way the organization does business. Doing this requires time, but it also requires that the organization set the stage so that such a transformation can occur.

Figure 10.01 identifies the major activities of this phase:

10.01: Create Supporting Infrastructure ◄━━━━━━━━━━

> ### Create Supporting Infrastructure
>
> *Strategy*
> • Strategize how to integrate Lean Six Sigma into existing infrastructure
>
> *Process*
> • Create a Lean Six Sigma communication plan to create pull
> • Procure or develop project tracking software
> • Procure or develop knowledge management software
> • Procure or develop reporting software

The first key to transformation is to ensure that continuous improvement is not the function of the quality department. Continuous improvement should be everyone's job. All too often, the quality function is held responsible and accountable for customer problems and continuous improvement. This is, upon consideration, absurd, as the quality function does not create the waste in the operational processes or produce defective products or services. Nor do they have the authority to restructure processes or departments to minimize waste or reduce defects; that authority rests with the functions. Therefore, all functions within the organization need to be made responsible for continuous-improvement efforts.

STRATEGY-RELATED ACTIVITIES

Strategize How to Integrate Lean Six Sigma into Existing Infrastructure

One of the keys to success is to integrate Lean Six Sigma (both people and support structures) into the organization's existing structures, rather than have a separate, independent structure to support the program. A common failing in many implementations is the opposite of integration; the organization structures the Lean Six Sigma program, both personnel and support systems, as a completely separate entity. This structure will almost certainly result in program failure because continuous improvement will then be viewed by most as the domain of others. Thus, there is no sense of ownership. Instead of being a part of the continuous-improvement process, most will view the Lean Six Sigma function as a nuisance to avoid, since projects detract from everyday activities. Further, those advocating such structures sometimes set up reward systems that provide benefits to the Lean Six Sigma group, to the exclusion of others. This creates a further rift, dooming the effort to failure. It is better to deploy human resources within the value streams and functions so as to merge continuous-improvement activities into the everyday way of doing business.

Likewise, the supporting infrastructure of processes and systems also needs to be integrated. For example, Lean Six Sigma needs to be integrated into human resources. As the program matures, it is key that the deployment team and steering committee work with human resources to ensure that Lean Six Sigma is woven into HR-led activities such as hiring and performance reviews. If the organization is to truly embrace the Lean Six Sigma methodology, then having prior Lean Six Sigma experience and training should, at some level, be melded into the diverse set of criteria the organization uses to select new hires. Likewise, it should be woven into the performance review process, and those who have Lean Six Sigma responsibilities should have them integrated into the criteria that will be used to periodically assess performance.

The compensation plan is one area you need to address if you are to successfully sustain Lean Six Sigma. There is a classic business paper titled, "On the folly of rewarding A, while hoping for B." In essence, it points out that employees will exhibit the behaviors for which companies reward them. It points out, for example, that companies often ask managers to deliver long-term growth, a focus on the customer, teamwork and synergy, and improvements in quality and productivity. However, at the same time, those companies often reward managers for cutting corners, making monthly or quarterly numbers, and their individual efforts rather than team effort. Lean Six Sigma is a long-term strategy for improving productivity, quality, and customer satisfaction. So if the reward systems run counter to Lean Six Sigma activities, the results will not be Lean Six Sigma results. The compensation system should reward improvements in value streams, not individual functions. Likewise, you should reward employees for long-term improvements in productivity, quality, and customer satisfaction, not just for achieving short-term goals.

The Lean Six Sigma communication plan discussed later in this chapter is another example of something that requires integration. It works best for Lean Six Sigma to be integrated into the existing organizational communication infrastructure. If, for example, there is a corporate newsletter, articles on Lean Six Sigma activities should be woven into the existing publication. Likewise, if an organizational manager holds a quarterly all-hands meeting, it is best to have an update on Lean Six Sigma provided as part of the regular meeting.

Failure to integrate into the existing structures will result in two major problems. First, it creates the perception that Lean Six Sigma is something separate from the everyday operation of the company. Second, it adds an unnecessary level of bureaucracy because you can use existing structures to achieve Lean Six Sigma's ends. You must avoid both of these if the program is to be sustainable.

At this early stage of the Lean Six Sigma program, the deployment team needs to strategize with value stream and functional leaders to determine how best to integrate Lean Six Sigma into the organization. Planning is the key. In phase 6, "Institutionalize the Program," these strategies will be executed.

PROCESS-RELATED ACTIVITIES

There are four process-related activities in this phase.

Create a Lean Six Sigma Communication Plan

The Lean Six Sigma communication plan and the execution of that plan will be critical factors in the early success of the Lean Six Sigma program. There are multiple constituencies that have a stake in the Lean Six Sigma program and each of these groups needs to be addressed.

Create a Pull System

The most important goal of the communication plan is to create pull for the Lean Six Sigma initiative. The first group that needs to be addressed is the managers in whose functional areas Lean Six Sigma will be launched. We would like to create a pull system for Lean Six Sigma training and projects. In this context, the term *pull system* means that management wants to use Lean Six Sigma as a methodology that can improve performance and is actively requesting (or pulling) Lean Six Sigma support. This is as opposed to Lean Six Sigma training and project facilitation being pushed onto managers. In order for Lean Six Sigma to work as a pull system, you must first show the organization how it can support achieving key business goals and objectives. Failure to illustrate how the methodology can enable attaining key strategies will result in a push system, whereby people are forced into the program rather than seeking it out. Later, it will be necessary to communicate project successes to the same groups to reinforce the benefits and ensure continued demand for the use of the methodology. An effective communication plan that clearly illustrates the value of the Lean Six Sigma methodology will prove invaluable in creating pull.

The communication that takes place as part of creating a pull system is also invaluable as a step in compiling the lists of potential projects noted earlier. As you communicate this information and create pull, you encourage managers to offer up potential projects for their areas.

Internal Communication

In addition to creating pull for the program, it is also important to communicate, at some level, with all the members of the organization. The more awareness everyone has of the program and the success it generates, the more positive the perception of the program will be. Additionally, the more people know about the program and the conceptual framework that underlies the methodology, the greater the impact on culture change.

It is highly likely that most of the people inside the organization will be affected by Lean Six Sigma projects at some point. Therefore, it is important that they be aware of the program's start-up as well as its progress and successes.

External Communication

It is also likely that external parties such as customers and suppliers will need to be communicated with, as they may be affected by the initiative. The communication with the customer base will most likely come through the sales force or others who regularly touch the customer. Communication with suppliers will likely come through the purchasing department or perhaps through the supplier quality function.

Communication with customers can serve several functions. As I mentioned in chapter 9, a robust project selection methodology is essential. Part of this robust project selection methodology is obtaining the voice of the customer. While the initial communication with the customer base will likely focus on communicating the benefits that the Lean Six Sigma program will create for customers over time, there is also the opportunity to obtain information from customers to enhance the organization's understanding of the voice of the customer. Integrating the ability to collect and process this feedback from customers is a value-added component of the communication plan.

Suppliers, in particular, need to be aware of the program, since it is probable that projects will at some point involve products or services that they supply. Significant sources of variation in a manufacturing facility often come from supplied materials or equipment. Likewise, waste reduction efforts often involve duplication of effort between suppliers and customers. Part of a waste reduction effort, therefore, is to work with suppliers to eliminate duplication and other forms of waste. These efforts are made easier by proactively communicating with the supply base about the Lean Six Sigma program and how they might be affected in the future.

Procure or Develop Project Tracking Software

Now the organization needs to decide about software to support the program: specifically, software involved in project tracking, knowledge management, and program recording. The size and complexity of software solutions required to support the program are very much a function of the size and complexity of the organization. Small organizations, such as those with a single location, require little in the way of software. In fact, many are able to successfully support the program using already existing software. However, large multinational organizations require an IT solution that allows personnel across the globe to track and report on the Lean Six Sigma program. Many organizations choose to develop their own in-house software; this allows them to fully customize the software to meet their unique needs. Others prefer to shop for off-the-shelf software.

The first need is software that will allow tracking of project progress. To reiterate, if the organization consists of a single-site operation, something as simple as an Excel® spreadsheet can be used to accomplish this function. However, if we are discussing multisite organizations or multinational corporations, a more sophisticated solution will be required.

On a macro level, the deployment teams must be able to see how many projects they have opened over a specific time frame, how many are currently active, and how many have closed. On a more micro level, it is also beneficial for the deployment teams to be able to see the current status of each project. Ideally, the organization will create a system that shows which phase of the DMAIC process each active project is in, and also shows its current status relative to the plan.

Procure or Develop Knowledge Management Software

Knowledge management, in relation to Lean Six Sigma, is the collection and dissemination of the knowledge gained from Lean Six Sigma projects. In larger organizations, software capable of supporting knowledge management is required. As teams undertake and complete Lean Six Sigma projects, they generate significant information and knowledge. It is imperative not to lose this knowledge and also to have a mechanism to actively share the knowledge with others who could benefit. This is the function of knowledge management.

One multinational organization with whom we have worked has developed its own in-house knowledge management system. The site they created contained a searchable database that housed all of the Lean Six Sigma projects undertaken globally. Black Belts and Green Belts entered the projects into the system using a standard methodology. As the Black Belts and Green Belts completed each phase of their Lean Six Sigma project, they uploaded documents into the system. Authorized users could then log on to the site, which could be accessed globally. The user then selected fields to search the database. For example, the user might search for all value-stream maps associated with hiring practices or for all designed experiments associated with injection molding. In this manner, Green Belts and Black Belts could access the database and draw from the knowledge generated by others' experience. This allowed the organization to achieve measurable savings, as it significantly reduced duplication of effort and sped up completion of additional projects.

Procure or Develop Reporting Software

Another need is a software application that facilitates the ability of management to view the performance of the program. It is necessary to have a mechanism whereby organizational leadership, deployment teams, and functional management have real-time access to information related to the Lean Six Sigma program. Basic pieces of information that are typically available include the number of projects opened, the number of projects completed, the areas in which the projects have been undertaken, types of processes on which the projects focused, and the benefits generated by the completed projects.

Create Supporting Infrastructure Checklist ◀━━━━━━━

	Applicable?	Not Completed	Completed

Strategy

1. Has a strategy for integrating Lean Six Sigma been developed? ☐ ☐ ☐

2. Has integration with HR been considered? ☐ ☐ ☐

3. Has integration with IT been considered? ☐ ☐ ☐

4. Has integration with Finance been considered? ☐ ☐ ☐

5. Has integration with Corporate Communciations been considered? ☐ ☐ ☐

6. Has integration with Operations been considered? ☐ ☐ ☐

7. Has integration with Marketing or Sales been considered? ☐ ☐ ☐

8. Has integration with Purchasing been considered? ☐ ☐ ☐

9. Has integration with Supply Chain been considered? ☐ ☐ ☐

10. Has integration with R&D or Product Development been considered? ☐ ☐ ☐

Process: Communication Plan

1. Has a detailed communciation plan been created? ☐ ☐ ☐

2. Does the plan address necessary internal customers? ☐ ☐ ☐

3. Does the plan address necessary external customers? ☐ ☐ ☐

4. Is the plan integrated with internal communication systems? ☐ ☐ ☐

5. Has the Corporate Communication function been engaged in the process of developing the plan? ☐ ☐ ☐

6. Will suppliers be communicated with regarding the Lean Six Sigma program? ☐ ☐ ☐

1 of 3 **Cont'd.** ━━━━▶

Create Supporting Infrastructure Checklist ◄▬▬▬▬▬

	Applicable?	Not Completed	Completed
Process: Communication Plan (Cont'd.)			
7. How will customers be communicated with regarding the Lean Six Sigma program?	☐	☐	☐
8. Has the sales force been trained to speak to customers about Lean Six Sigma?	☐	☐	☐
9. Will the company speak at conferences?	☐	☐	☐
10. Will the company publish results in articles?	☐	☐	☐
11. At what standard meetings or events will Lean Six Sigma be a mandatory part of the agenda?	☐	☐	☐
Project Selection and Queuing			
1. Will software for project queuing be required?	☐	☐	☐
2. Where will the queued lists of potential projects be stored?	☐	☐	☐
3. Will there be open read-write access to the potential projects listing?	☐	☐	☐
4. If not, has it been determined who will have read-write access to the potential projects queue?	☐	☐	☐
5. Will the project queuing and project tracking software be integrated?	☐	☐	☐
Project Tracking and Review			
1. Has a system for tracking projects been established?	☐	☐	☐
2. Has it been determined who will have access to ongoing and completed projects?	☐	☐	☐
3. Will the project tracking system require that certain fields be entered or that certain files be provided to standardize sequencing of project events?	☐	☐	☐

Create Supporting Infrastructure Checklist ◀━━━━━━

	Applicable?	Not Completed	Completed

Project Summing and Reporting

1. Has it been determined what information management requires at each level? ☐ ☐ ☐

2. Has it been determined who will have access to project summary data? ☐ ☐ ☐

3. Has IT been engaged to assist in developing a system for summing project gains and creating a set of management reports? ☐ ☐ ☐

4. Has Finance been engaged to assist in developing a system for summing project gains and creating a set of management reports? ☐ ☐ ☐

5. Have personnel requiring face-to-face report-outs been identified? ☐ ☐ ☐

6. Has reporting frequency been determined? ☐ ☐ ☐

Knowledge Management

1. Has IT been engaged to assist in a technology solution? ☐ ☐ ☐

2. Will software for knowledge management be developed or procured? ☐ ☐ ☐

3. How searchable will the database be (e.g., by product line, product, tools used, problem type)? ☐ ☐ ☐

4. Will BB statistical software be globally standardized? ☐ ☐ ☐

5. Has statistical analysis software been identified and procured by the organization? ☐ ☐ ☐

CHAPTER 11

IDENTIFY AND DEPLOY RESOURCES

In the **fifth** phase, "Identify and Deploy Resources," we finally begin the training of Black Belts, Green Belts, and others who will lead and support the Lean Six Sigma project teams. Hopefully, by this point in the book you understand why jumping into training without setting up the necessary support systems and structures creates a significant risk in terms of both project and program failure.

Specific activities to undertake in this phase of the deployment process are:

11.01: Identify and Deploy Resources ◀━━━━━━━━━━

Identify and Deploy Resources

Strategy
• Identify Black Belt and Green Belt candidates

Process
• Execute training rollout strategy
• Train Black Belts and Green Belts
• Identify and mentor potential Master Black Belt candidates

STRATEGY-RELATED ACTIVITIES

There is one strategy-related activity in the fifth phase.

Identify Black Belt and Green Belt Candidates

The first step in this phase is to identify high-potential candidates for the remaining roles and responsibilities of the Lean Six Sigma program.

11.02 Lean Six Sigma Resources: People

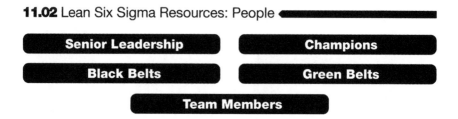

Just as leaders needed to identify the right individuals as deployment Champions, they need to identify the correct individuals to fill the remaining positions, which are associated with project team staffing. Failing to give due consideration to who will be selected for project leadership and related responsibilities will increase the risk of project failures.

Master Black Belts are former Black Belts who have exhibited a mastery of the Lean Six Sigma process and have vast experience in its application. Master Black Belts typically serve as mentors and coaches to the Green Belts and Black Belts leading the teams.

Black Belts and Green Belts are the people who lead Lean Six Sigma project teams. As I noted earlier, either a Black Belt or a Green Belt can lead a team (if you don't anticipate that the project will require Black Belt–level tools). If the project is more complex and will require the use of Black Belt–level tools, it is not appropriate to task the Green Belt with leading the team.

Some practitioners subscribe to what might be termed a cookie-cutter formula in terms of program staffing. Typical of this approach is to train one Black Belt for every 100 employees, 10 Green Belts for every Black Belt, and one Master Black Belt for every 25 Black Belts.

In reality, the number of Master Black Belts, Black Belts, and Green Belts needing training should be determined by the program's goals and objectives that were developed back in phase 1 – "Engage

Leaders" (see chapter 7). Using goal information in conjunction with the projected number of projects per person per year and the anticipated average benefit per project, you can determine the number of resources you will require to support the program.

One of the questions one must address at the beginning of this phase is: "Will the organization be training just Black Belts, just Green Belts, or both?" There is no single correct answer to this question, as any of the three options may be viable depending on organizational circumstances and the history of continuous-improvement efforts. If the organization does not have a history of continuous-improvement efforts, training only Green Belts may be a viable option at the inception of the program. In this circumstance, there is generally much "low-hanging fruit" scattered throughout the organization. (Low-hanging fruit are those things that are easy to fix, as opposed to hard to fix fruit that is high in the tree). Green Belt–level skills may be sufficient to gather low-hanging fruit.

On the other hand, if the organization has a history of continuous-improvement efforts, it is likely that Black Belt–level skills will be necessary to generate improvement at the desired rate. Generally, in most organizations a combination of Black Belts and Green Belts is necessary to most effectively and efficiently achieve the organization's goals.

You should also note that Black Belts and Green Belts can work on projects outside their area of expertise. Black Belts and Green Belts are experts in the DMAIC methodology. As such, they can lead teams and successfully complete projects as long as team members who have strong knowledge of the process support them.

Champions

The role of the Champion is to select projects, provide the resources necessary to successfully complete the projects, and remove barriers to team progress.

Champions, by virtue of the role they fill, must be relatively senior people within the organization. That is, the Champion must be high enough in the organization that he or she controls the resources necessary for team success. If the Champion does not control the resources necessary for team success, project failure is more likely. Therefore, the more complex the project is and the more functional areas it cuts across, the more senior the Champion needs to be.

11.03: Champions (Sponsors)

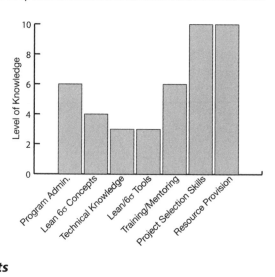

- Responsible for:
  - Project selection and approval
  - Providing resources
  - Removing barriers

- Not full-time Lean Six Sigma

- Sometimes called project sponsors

- Champions are responsible for project success

Master Black Belts

The definition of a Master Black Belt is unclear because it tends to vary from organization to organization. These differences are often due to the diversity of responsibilities assigned to Master Black Belts across organizations. One approach, taken by some organizations, is that the Master Black Belts are coaches and mentors to the Black Belts and Green Belts undertaking Lean Six Sigma projects. In this scenario they have an extremely strong skill set in terms of Lean Six Sigma tools and techniques and the ability to effectively train, communicate with, coach, and mentor the project leaders. Some organizations view Master Black Belts as concurrently serving a second function; that function is to serve as the strategic liaison between the leadership of the organization and the Lean Six Sigma program. Put another way, Master Black Belts would be key components of the steering committees both at the organizational and business unit level. Either way, Master Black Belts are always people formerly at the Black Belt level that have extremely strong Lean Six Sigma skills in addition to a well-established record of success.

Black Belts

Black Belts form the backbone of the Lean Six Sigma program. Often referred to as agents of change, they are the people who will likely lead a significant proportion of the Lean Six Sigma teams.

11.04: Black Belts

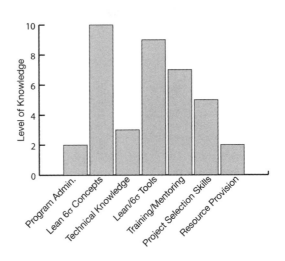

- Respected, high-caliber employees

- Responsible for:
  - Leading LSS teams
  - Being agents of change
  - Applying all LSS tools

- Backbone of the LSS program

- Full-time or part-time LSS resource

Figure 11.04 illustrates the skills required of Black Belts. It is most critical that they are expert in the Lean Six Sigma concepts and tools, and also have the ability to mentor and train Green Belts and team members. Selecting the appropriate people to be trained as Black Belts is a key to successful program implementation, as these are the people that will be leading the improvement project efforts. When looking at who should be trained as a Black Belt, there are two sets of skills to consider: hard and soft skills. Hard skills are quantitative in nature and include such things as knowledge and skill with data, statistics, and computer applications. Soft skills are people and personality related: effective communication, good negotiation, willingness to make change, tenacity, and good leadership are some of the attributes. When considering the candidates, it is important that a minimum level of soft skills be present, regardless of the strength of the hard skills.

Green Belts

Green Belts are effectively junior Black Belts, as they will often lead project teams that do not require Black Belt–level skills.

11.05: Green Belts ◄━━━━━━━━━━━━━━━━━━━━━━━━━━

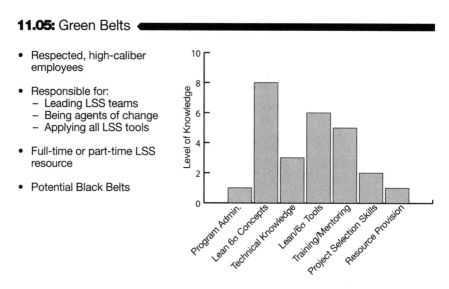

- Respected, high-caliber employees

- Responsible for:
  - Leading LSS teams
  - Being agents of change
  - Applying all LSS tools

- Full-time or part-time LSS resource

- Potential Black Belts

The skills in figure 11.05 are similar to those of the Black Belts, but the level of expertise is generally lower. As I noted previously, Green Belts can support Black Belts on project teams or they can lead Lean Six Sigma teams themselves. Which strategy an organization pursues is primarily driven by the maturity of prior continuous-improvement efforts. Often, if an organization does not have an established history of continuous improvement, it may be sufficient to train only Green Belts and have them lead all of the project teams. Green Belts leading teams is more common in service environments, as service-based functions and organizations are relatively recent arrivals to the concept of formal continuous improvement. Manufacturing initially embraced formal continuous improvement over a generation ago. As a result, manufacturers typically harvested any low-hanging fruit years ago. Therefore, Green Belts are less likely to be able to successfully lead teams in these environments; Black Belt–level skills are required to solve the more difficult problems in this environment.

Team Members

Team members are process experts who support Black Belts and Green Belts in the continuous-improvement effort. Black Belts and Green Belts, as I noted earlier, do not need to be experts in the process targeted for improvement. To compensate for this lack of process expertise, it is necessary to choose team members who have the requisite process knowledge and skills that will enable the team to successfully complete the project. The number of team members will be a function of the size and complexity of the project.

Yellow Belts

Often, the organization will train project team members as Yellow Belts. This type of training focuses primarily on awareness and general knowledge rather than on skills that would allow the individual to lead a team. The goal of such training is an awareness of how Lean Six Sigma delivers benefits and an ability to participate more productively as a member of a team. Such training normally covers the conceptual framework of Lean Six Sigma and general awareness of the methodology. The need for Yellow Belt training is primarily a function of the goals and objectives laid out by the leadership in phase 1 of the Deployment Roadmap. Such training normally runs between one-half to two full days.

If one of the goals of the Lean Six Sigma program is to begin to effect changes to the organizational culture, training personnel as Yellow Belts is essential. To effect cultural change, it is necessary that a critical mass of people support continuous improvement and the conceptual framework and use of Lean Six Sigma. Merely training a relatively small proportion of the employees as Green Belts and Black Belts will be insufficient to obtain this critical mass and position the organization for cultural change. The other consideration that will affect the need for Yellow Belt training is the number of concurrent projects necessary to meet leadership's goals and the level of complexity of those projects. The greater the project demand, the more beneficial it will be to have people trained as Yellow Belts.

Allocating Time to Projects

As the teams begin working on projects, it is imperative that the Champions ensure the Black Belts and Green Belts have sufficient time to dedicate to them. Just as starving the **program** of resources will lead to program atrophy, starving a **project** of resources will result in project failure. The problem most commonly encountered is the time conflict that Green Belts and Black Belts face with their functional responsibilities. Their managers often see those functional responsibilities as more urgent than the Lean Six Sigma efforts. As a result, the Lean Six Sigma projects are shuffled to the back burner while functional responsibilities are met. The rationale, of course, is that delaying a Lean Six Sigma project by a day or two will not meaningfully affect the organization. The problem is that when the Lean Six Sigma project is repeatedly shuffled to the back burner, significant delays begin to accrue, both management and team support dwindle, project failure rates increase markedly, and the morale of the entire organization can suffer.

From a continuous-improvement perspective, the ideal situation is that significant resources are readily available and that Green Belts and Black Belts have 100 percent of their time allocated to their Lean Six Sigma projects. However, this may not always be practical or possible. Even so, it is still the responsibility of the Champions to ensure that sufficient time is allocated. Experience has shown that Black Belts and Green Belts must dedicate a minimum of 25 percent of their time to the project if it is to be successfully completed. If anything less than 25 percent of the team leader's time is dedicated to the project, the duration will begin to stretch out due to lack of resource commitment. The longer a project takes to complete, the higher the risk of failure. As time goes on, priorities change; competing resource needs will arise and changes in team responsibilities and roles will occur. All of these things jeopardize successful project completion.

If you expect that dedicating sufficient time to projects will be a challenge, then you will need to put targeted strategies in place to overcome this issue, to better ensure success. For example, rather than assigning a single Black Belt or Green Belt to the project, assign multiple Green Belts and Black Belts to the same project; two Belts can then share the responsibility. In doing this, however, you should recognize that there are inherent inefficiencies in such a structure. Whenever management responsibilities are shared, there is an increased need for communication and a heightened risk of duplicated effort, missed essential tasks, or delays. Experience has shown that if two people share the responsibility for leading a project, it does cut the average workload somewhat, but it does not, in any way, cut the workload in half.

Another solution to time constraints is to temporarily remove the Green Belt or Black Belt from his or her normal, day-to-day functional responsibilities. You then allocate those responsibilities among a group of the Green Belt's or Black Belt's functional peers. While this, in theory, frees up 100 percent of the Green Belt's or Black Belt's time, the reality is that perhaps 75 percent of their time is actually freed up from functional responsibilities. During the several weeks or months that the project is under way, the Green Belt or Black Belt is able to dedicate the majority of his or her time to successful project completion. This not only increases the probability of the project's success, but also reduces total project duration. Upon the project's completion, the Green

Belt or Black Belt returns to his or her functional responsibilities. In this way, you can cycle Green Belts and Black Belts into and out of Lean Six Sigma project activity.

PROCESS-RELATED ACTIVITIES

Execute Training Rollout Strategy

The product of creating a training rollout strategy is the list of people to be trained as well as a schedule associated with their training. In phase 2, "Create Deployment Plans," the deployment teams set goals for each business unit and create plans to support the achievement of those goals. One of the key things that the teams identify at this time is the number of people who need training at each level of each business unit to support the Lean Six Sigma program. Specifically, the teams determine the number of Black Belts, Green Belts, and other personnel needing training to support project efforts. The training rollout strategy specifies the number of personnel to train at each level, the number of waves of training, and the time frame for each wave (spacing between waves to minimize resource issues).

11.06: Lean Six Sigma: A Top-Down Program

The mistake less successful programs often make is that they do not adequately train Champions in how to properly select projects and support the project teams. If the Champions have not been adequately trained, there is not only a risk of poorly selected projects that do not support key organizational goals, but there is also a risk that the projects will be poorly scoped, thus increasing the risk of project failure. Even if the Champion properly selects the projects, if the Champion is not sufficiently knowledgeable on how to support the team, the team faces an increased risk of failure.

If training is to take place in an organized and systematic fashion, deployment teams must create and execute a training plan. Because the leaders and Champions were trained back in phase 2, the remaining training centers on the Black Belts, Green Belts, and Yellow Belts.

The training plan lays out the timing of the various training events that will take place during deployment. How the various events are sequenced and spaced out chronologically is based on many factors including the volume of training, availability of personnel, geographic challenges, and desired outcomes. For example, many organizations find it desirable to have the Black Belts or Green Belts train the Yellow Belts. If this is the plan, you will need to train the Black Belts and Green Belts far enough in advance that they are ready to conduct the Yellow Belt training.

Most organizations use an outside consultant for most of the Black Belt and Green Belt training. Over time, as the organization develops Master Black Belts and Black Belts gain more experience, the training can be brought in-house. The consultant can assist the deployment teams in the construction of a viable training plan.

It is here, in phase 5, that you execute the training plan and begin projects.

Train Black Belts and Green Belts

Black Belts

Black Belt training typically consists of 20 days of classroom training divided into four one-week increments; these increments are about one month apart. The purpose of separating the increments by one month is to afford the Black Belt and the Lean Six Sigma team the opportunity to progress through the project during the training, using what they learned with the support of the trainer. The end result is that projects are completed shortly after the training, providing rapid payback on the investment in training.

Before the first training session, the Black Belt and Champion will work together to select a Lean Six Sigma project. This allows the Black Belt to apply tools and methods from the training directly to the project during training, which aids in the learning process and increases project efficiency.

In the subsequent weeks of training, Black Belts report on their progress at the start of each training session. This allows for both instructor and peer review. At the close of each of the four week-long sessions, the Black Belts report their anticipated activities and how they envision applying the tools and techniques taught in that session to their projects.

While certification requirements vary between organizations, the minimum requirement for certification as a Black Belt is the successful completion of at least one Lean Six Sigma Black Belt project.

Green Belts

Green Belt training typically consists of 10 days of classroom training separated into two one-week increments. Depending on the role of Green Belts within the organization, the Green Belts may or may not arrive at the first training session with assigned projects. If their task is completing projects, the training and project presentations are similar to that for the Black Belts.

Typically, if projects are assigned, the Green Belt will be required to successfully complete the project in order to obtain certification. If projects are not mandatory, then the training typically uses a posttest for determining whether to award certification.

Identify and Mentor Potential Master Black Belt Candidates

When an organization undertakes the implementation of a Lean Six Sigma program, it typically uses the services of an outside consulting and training firm. However, as time goes on, the organization often develops its own internal resources and lessens its dependency on external suppliers. To this end, the organization should identify potential Master Black Belts as early as possible, who eventually will be internal consultants and trainers.

Beginning with the first several waves of Black Belt training, the organization should seek to identify high-potential Black Belts who can eventually rise to the level of Master Black Belt. It should monitor these candidates over time and provide coaching from the external consulting group. The coaching should focus on providing not only additional expertise in the tools and techniques of Lean Six Sigma, but also on assessing and inculcating skills necessary to mentor, train, and perform other Master Black Belt tasks.

Identify and Deploy Resources Checklist ◄━━━━━━━━

	Applicable?	Not Completed	Completed

Black Belt Resources

		Applicable?	Not Completed	Completed
1.	Will the BBs be full-time?	☐	☐	☐
2.	Has the number of BBs required to achieve objectives been calculated?	☐	☐	☐
3.	Has a job description been prepared for the BB position?	☐	☐	☐
4.	Have BB selection criteria been developed?	☐	☐	☐
5.	Who will select the BB candidates?	☐	☐	☐
6.	Have personnel been identified for all anticipated BB roles?	☐	☐	☐
7.	Have plans been made to backfill positions so that the BBs can move into their new roles?	☐	☐	☐
8.	Has a BB training schedule been developed?	☐	☐	☐
9.	Have potential BBs met with the appropriate deployment Champion to understand the BB role and expectations of the BB?	☐	☐	☐
10.	Has the number and size of projects BBs will be expected to carry been determined?	☐	☐	☐
11.	Has a BB rotation schedule been developed?	☐	☐	☐

Green Belt Resources

		Applicable?	Not Completed	Completed
1.	Has the number of GBs required to support BBs been calculated?	☐	☐	☐
2.	Has a job description been prepared for the GB position?	☐	☐	☐
3.	Have GB selection criteria been developed?	☐	☐	☐
4.	What percentage of time will GBs support BB projects?	☐	☐	☐
5.	Have personnel been identified for all anticipated GB roles?	☐	☐	☐

1 of 3 **Cont'd.** ■━━━━►

Identify and Deploy Resources Checklist

	Applicable?	Not Completed	Completed

Green Belt Resources (Cont'd.)

6. Has a GB training schedule been developed? ☐ ☐ ☐

7. Have potential GBs met with the appropriate deployment Champion to understand the GB role and expectations of the GB? ☐ ☐ ☐

Master Black Belt Resources

1. Has the number of MBBs needed to support the BBs been determined? ☐ ☐ ☐

2. Will MBBs be hired, developed, or both? ☐ ☐ ☐

3. Has interim MBB support been arranged? ☐ ☐ ☐

4. Has a job description been prepared for the MBB position? ☐ ☐ ☐

5. Have MBB selection criteria been developed? ☐ ☐ ☐

6. How will potential MBB candidates be identified? ☐ ☐ ☐

7. Have all MBB candidates met with the deployment Champion to understand the role of the MBB and expectations? ☐ ☐ ☐

8. Have all MBB candidates met with business unit leadership to understand the role of the MBB and expectations? ☐ ☐ ☐

Training Resources

1. Have MBB consulting services arrangements been made? ☐ ☐ ☐

2. Have material licensing arrangements been made? ☐ ☐ ☐

3. Is a plan in place to identify MBB and BB candidates to lead waves of future training (i.e., a train-the-trainer strategy)? ☐ ☐ ☐

2 of 3 **Cont'd.** ➡

Identify and Deploy Resources Checklist ◀━━━━━━━━━━

	Applicable?	Not Completed	Completed
Future Resources			
1. Has a plan been put in place to minimize turnover of BBs and GBs?	☐	☐	☐
2. Has a plan been put in place to rotate BBs into and back out of the Lean Six Sigma program?	☐	☐	☐
3. Has a plan been put in place for training of additional BBs and GBs to compensate for turnover?	☐	☐	☐
4. Have future MBB, BB, and GB needs been projected for the next three years?	☐	☐	☐
5. Is a plan in place to select future MBB, BB, and GB candidates?	☐	☐	☐
6. How will future high-potential BBs be identified for consideration as MBBs?	☐	☐	☐
7. How will future high-potential GBs be identified for consideration as BBs?	☐	☐	☐

CHAPTER 12

INSTITUTIONALIZE THE PROGRAM

It is finally in this **sixth** phase of the Deployment Roadmap that the organization directly addresses the evolution from a program to a way of doing business. Ultimately, as previously stated, the goal is not to merely have a Lean Six Sigma program, but rather to have Lean Six Sigma incorporated into the organization's culture and how it does its business. Obviously, this cultural shift takes place over a period of years. The time required to transition from a program to a way of doing business is a function of leadership's commitment to the philosophy and use of Lean Six Sigma. If management is truly committed to the use of continuous improvement throughout the organization, this transition will begin quickly; if not, then the shift in culture will take far longer, if it happens at all. Making the shift happen is the focus of phase 6, "Institutionalize the Program."

THE LEAN SIX SIGMA MATURITY MODEL

If Lean Six Sigma is to become woven into the organizational fabric, it needs to function at a high level of maturity, as defined by the Maturity Model shown in this chapter. The organization's continuous-improvement efforts generate a progression in its business results. The long-term goal of Lean Six Sigma deployment is to move the organization from its current state to an optimizing state, at which point Lean Six Sigma is no longer a program, but an integrated part of the way the company conducts its day-to-day business and delivers maximum business results.

Initial Level

In the Initial level, organizational leadership often does not support the process-improvement efforts and may not even know how to do so.

Due to economic disruptions, many organizations have regressed in recent years from a more mature level back to the Initial level as part of short-term survival strategies. Many organizations that had more mature continuous-improvement programs effectively dismantled them in the rush to cut short-term costs due to drastic decreases in revenue.

The result of the cutbacks was a regression in, or even elimination of, such efforts. This phenomenon creates an additional set of challenges to implementing Lean Six Sigma, as the message sent to associates is that continuous improvement is not a core activity and that management will sacrifice it. Unfortunately, this is the signal received in these circumstances, regardless of leadership's intent and its justification of sacrificing long-term success for short-term survival.

In the Initial level, process-improvement efforts are misguidedly seen as a luxury, not a necessity. It is not that management does not see improvement as desirable, but that it expects improvement to happen without any investment or commitment to making it happen. Therefore it does not invest in its people or its processes.

Because management is not engaged, there is no continuous improvement organization; all activity is ad hoc. Typically, during the firefighting that dominates organizational activity, the organization slaps short-term fixes on processes, which have no lasting impact and result in the same problems cycling back repeatedly. Occasionally, as part of the firefighting efforts, the organization stumbles on a process improvement that is not a short-term fix and real continuous improvement accidentally results.

12.01: Lean Six Sigma Maturity Model

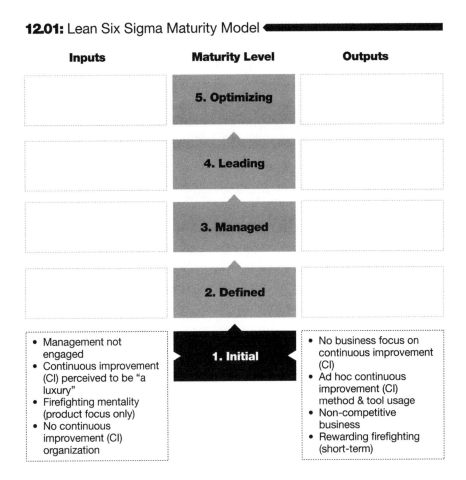

Inputs	Maturity Level	Outputs
	5. Optimizing	
	4. Leading	
	3. Managed	
	2. Defined	
• Management not engaged • Continuous improvement (CI) perceived to be "a luxury" • Firefighting mentality (product focus only) • No continuous improvement (CI) organization	1. Initial	• No business focus on continuous improvement (CI) • Ad hoc continuous improvement (CI) method & tool usage • Non-competitive business • Rewarding firefighting (short-term)

Defined Level

When a program moves into the Defined level, there is improvement relative to the Initial level, but the program is far from robust. At the Defined level, organizational leadership has evolved from perceiving process improvement as a luxury to perceiving it as something that is desirable. In spite of the evolution in perspective, support is still limited and efforts are undertaken by a makeshift organization that is significantly underresourced. The makeshift organization does not yet embrace process thinking, and primary efforts focus on product control rather than process control. As a result, most activity is still reactive rather than proactive and preventive.

At this level of maturity, continuous-improvement efforts have little impact on the organizational results. Because leadership is not engaged, activities are not focused on key business objectives. Thus, resources expended on process and product improvement yield very limited benefit. While there is some use of generally accepted continuous-improvement methods, such use is composed mostly of basic tools rather than more sophisticated methods, and their usage is not uniform, even within the continuous-improvement function. Lastly, the organization allows employees to "game the system." That is, the organization evaluates performance based on product measures of quality and firefighting activities, and rework loops are not punished, but rewarded.

12.02: Lean Six Sigma Maturity Model

Inputs	Maturity Level	Outputs
	5. Optimizing	
	4. Leading	
	3. Managed	
• Management aware, tacit support • CI perceived to be desirable • Product focus driving ad hoc process focus • Makeshift CI organization	2. Defined	• CI efforts not focused on key business goals • Basic mgt. of CI tool & method usage • Marginally competitive business • Reward "gaming" the system
	1. Initial	

Managed Level

The jump from Defined to Managed is a significant one. It is at this level of maturity that management is meaningfully supporting continuous-improvement efforts. Because leadership perceives continuous improvement to be necessary for business success, there is sufficient support for the creation of a cohesive and well-resourced organization. It is this increased level of support and the creation of a cohesive organization which allows the organizational thinking to begin evolving from product control to process control. Unfortunately, while the organization is beginning the evolution from product to process thinking, it still views process improvement as the responsibility of the continuous-improvement function. That is, the organization still does not view it as the responsibility of everyone in the organization, only of those specifically tasked with the responsibility.

At this level, the continuous-improvement efforts become focused on key business goals and objectives. The evolution in leaders' thinking means that they are at last engaged in the effort, and this engagement allows for the communication necessary to properly direct continuous-improvement activity. The increased leadership support also creates an evolution from ad hoc use of individual tools and methods, to a more uniform use of recognized continuous-improvement methodologies in improvement efforts. Because of the linkage between leadership and the continuous-improvement function, as well as the use of recognized tools and methods, activities now contribute to improved business results.

Leading Level

This level of maturity can only be achieved when the leadership of the organization actually understands the conceptual framework of continuous improvement and comprehends how it provides a competitive advantage. This change in thinking represents a major shift in organizational culture; with this level of leadership understanding comes full support for such efforts. At this level of conceptual understanding, the organization has matured such that continuous-improvement efforts primarily focus on process control, a proactive, preventive approach to quality, productivity, and customer satisfaction. Perhaps more important, the continuous-improvement function begins its evolution from being responsible for generating results through direct activity, to being a catalyst for others to generate continuous improvement. That is, the culture has shifted to one in which process improvement is everyone's responsibility.

12.03: Lean Six Sigma Maturity Model

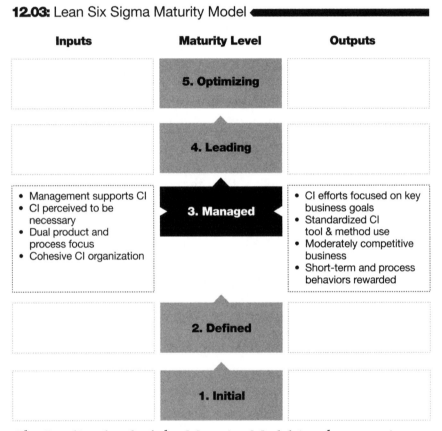

Inputs	Maturity Level	Outputs
	5. Optimizing	
	4. Leading	
• Management supports CI • CI perceived to be necessary • Dual product and process focus • Cohesive CI organization	3. Managed	• CI efforts focused on key business goals • Standardized CI tool & method use • Moderately competitive business • Short-term and process behaviors rewarded
	2. Defined	
	1. Initial	

The Leading level of the Maturity Model is where continuous improvement becomes a competitive advantage for the organization. Because leadership conceptually understands continuous improvement, its implementation, and how its culture can drive competitive advantage, the organization follows its leadership in undergoing a transformation. Improvement activities throughout the organization focus on business imperatives and the focus is consistent across all areas of the organization. Continuous improvement is no longer the province of a stand-alone function. Additionally, the organization integrates continuous-improvement tools and methods into a synergistic system (e.g., Lean Six Sigma) that provides a structure (e.g., DMAIC) for the tools' use. Additionally, the organization has put in place systems and structures that support proactive process-improvement efforts. For example, project selection is a formalized process, as is knowledge management. The power of knowledge related to improvement efforts is recognized and structured systems are in place to ensure that the knowledge gained is disseminated to all applicable areas for maximum benefit.

12.04: Lean Six Sigma Maturity Model ◄━━━━━━━━

Inputs	Maturity Level	Outputs
	5. Optimizing	
• Management understands & fully supports CI • CI perceived to enable business success • Process focus primary • CI organization is catalyst for improvement	4. Leading	• CI used to gain competitive advantage • CI methods integrated together • Highly competitive business • Knowledge leveraged for further gain • Long-term and process behaviors rewarded
	3. Managed	
	2. Defined	
	1. Initial	

Another key change in organizational culture that takes place at this level is an evolution from short-term to long-term thinking. At this level of maturity, leaders recognize the long-term business benefits of enhancing quality and customer satisfaction. So, leaders will support activities that may not yield short-term benefits if they can gain long-term benefits. Financial returns (e.g., making the quarterly numbers) are not the sole criterion for determining where to expend organizational resources.

Optimizing Level

This final level represents the epitome of continuous-improvement culture and performance. To reach this point of maturity, the leadership of the organization, in its actions and behaviors, must embody the philosophy and methodology of continuous improvement. This embodiment must also fully cascade down such that the entire organization focuses on continuous improvement as part of day-to-day activities. Continuous improvement is a constant consideration in leadership and management decision making at both the strategic and the tactical levels.

At the Optimizing level, the organizational culture has fully transformed from its prior state and has fully embraced the philosophy of continually striving to improve. In other words, continuous improvement has become embedded in the organizational culture and the core business processes.

Also at this level, process thinking pervades the organization and improvement activities focus on proactive, preventive measures. The organization assesses new processes and potential process changes and takes preventive measures before implementation to minimize the risk of process breakdowns reducing productivity or jeopardizing customer deliverables. The organization has significantly reduced or eliminated product-control efforts where possible.

The continuous-improvement function, at this level of maturity, has evolved from being a catalyst in the Leading phase to being embedded directly in the organizational value streams and functions. That is, the continuous-improvement function is truly woven into the fabric of the organization. At this level, continuous improvement is a core competency from which the organization derives a strong strategic advantage.

12.05: Lean Six Sigma Maturity Model

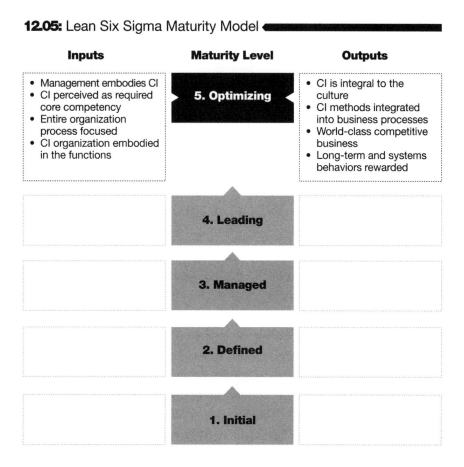

INSTITUTIONALIZE THE PROGRAM

This phase of the Deployment Roadmap, "Institutionalize the Program," concerns ensuring that the organization undertakes the transition from a program to a way of doing business at the appropriate time and with the necessary rigor. Specific activities in this phase are:

12.06: Institutionalize the Program ◄━━━━━━━━━━━━━━━

Institutionalize the Program

Strategy
- Create joint integration plans with key value streams and functions

Process
- Integrate with existing systems and structures
  - Communication
  - Finance
  - Human Resources
  - Information Technology
  - Sales
  - Operations
- Initiate management coaching program

Phase 4, "Create Supporting Infrastructure," initiates planning of the integration of Lean Six Sigma into the fabric of the organization. In this phase, comprehensive implementation of these integration plans is executed.

STRATEGY-RELATED ACTIVITIES

Create Joint Integration Plans with Key Value Streams and Functions

Once the Lean Six Sigma initiative is up and running and the first wave of projects has demonstrated the benefits of the Lean Six Sigma methodology, it is time to begin engaging functional and value stream leaders in planning. Prior to the first one or two waves of projects, leaders and managers often will not be ready to engage in a discussion around planning for future Lean Six Sigma activities in their area of responsibility. First, it is not until they are able to personally observe the benefits of Lean Six Sigma that they will be willing to commit the time required to think through long-term planning around the topic of continuous improvement and Lean Six Sigma. (If managers and leaders with prior exposure to Lean Six Sigma are willing to engage in this earlier, then the opportunity should be seized as soon as possible.) Secondly, it is often not until a couple of waves of projects have been undertaken that the managers and leaders will understand what needs to be integrated and why. In other words, they need to see it for themselves before they are willing and able to undertake value-added integration planning.

Because this planning involves key strategic issues (e.g., how the organization interfaces and works with suppliers and customers, employee career progression, and information technology infrastructure), senior leaders will need to be engaged in this aspect of planning. Once the big-picture issues are agreed upon by the leaders, the detailed planning can be delegated to the appropriate level.

For each of the applicable areas, a strategic plan (of what is to be integrated and how to carry out this integration) needs to be developed. Each plan should have a list of specific activities, along with timing and responsibility for each task, clearly identified. The exact format of the plan is not critical. For example, some organizations prefer an action item format, while others use Gantt charts or other project planning tools.

Lastly, those responsible for the deployment and sustainment of Lean Six Sigma should recognize that while these plans can be created in a relatively short period of time, the execution of a significant proportion of the plans will take place over months and, even more likely, years.

PROCESS-RELATED ACTIVITIES

Phase 6 has two process-related activities, that cut across many systems and structures.

Integrate with Existing Systems and Structures

At a tactical level, integrating the program with existing systems and structures will help institutionalize it and make it part of the way your organization does business. It is key not to have a Lean Six Sigma program per se. Rather, it is best to smoothly integrate the Lean Six Sigma program into everyday processes, not make it a special set of processes outside the everyday activities. To do this, those charged with deployment must, to the greatest degree possible, integrate it into existing systems rather than create new ones. Specific examples of areas into whose processes you should integrate Lean Six Sigma include:

- Communication
- Finance
- Human Resources
- Information Technology
- Sales
- Operations

There are several ways you can weave Lean Six Sigma efforts into the existing HR infrastructure. One example would be to consider prior Lean Six Sigma experience as part of the formal hiring criteria used by the organization. Another example would be to consider Lean Six Sigma success as part of the employee evaluation system. That is, if Lean Six Sigma is going to be part of the organization's way of conducting its business, then it should be part of the systems that leaders use to operate the organization.

A second example is the organization's communication systems. It is not desirable to have a separate communication system to inform employees about Lean Six Sigma activities. You should piggyback onto the organization's existing communication systems. For example, you can have articles integrated into the existing newsletter, of how the Lean Six Sigma program is affecting the organization, and integrate such information into the CEO's all-hands meetings and periodic e-mails on the state of the business.

Initiate Management Coaching Program

When a Lean Six Sigma program is implemented organization-wide, many people who have responsibilities associated with the program, or whose area of responsibility is affected by the program, will not have a background in continuous improvement or continuous-improvement methodologies. Often, these individuals will struggle to understand how to correctly carry out their Lean Six Sigma program responsibilities. A coaching program can assist these people and successfully support the Lean Six Sigma program.

In such a program, you assign coaches with a background in continuous improvement and Lean Six Sigma to the executives and managers, who can then successfully carry out the actions and exhibit the behaviors necessary to support the Lean Six Sigma program. The coach's level within the organization should be as equivalent as possible to that of the executive. For example, director-level personnel within the continuous-improvement function would coach directors outside the continuous-improvement function.

The coaching includes the coach defining a set of activities and a set of behaviors that the individual should follow as part of supporting the Lean Six Sigma initiative. For example, a plant manager should discuss the status of the Lean Six Sigma program at the monthly all-hands meeting he or she conducts with employees. The coach would help the manager to understand the behaviors and activities needed and will coach her or him on how to successfully carry out those activities and behaviors. The coach also provides ongoing feedback to the manager.

I should note that the coaching program augments the mentor-mentee relationship that exists naturally within the organization. It does not replace it. If the organizational culture, formally or informally, encourages the development of mentor-mentee relationships, then it is best to integrate Lean Six Sigma understanding and performance into that dynamic.

Institutionalize the Program Checklist ◀━━━━━━━━

	Applicable?	Not Completed	Completed

Strategy

1. Have joint plans for Lean Six Sigma been developed with key value streams, functions, and businesses? ☐ ☐ ☐

2. Is there a structured method for updating plans? ☐ ☐ ☐

3. Is there a feedback loop for measuring performance vs. goals? ☐ ☐ ☐

Process

Communication

1. Is there a process to regularly review corporate communication strategy and ensure Lean Six Sigma is incorporated into the strategy? ☐ ☐ ☐

2. Are executives and managers part of the internal communication strategy at all levels? ☐ ☐ ☐

Finance

1. Is Finance involved in determining financial project selection criteria? ☐ ☐ ☐

2. Does Finance lead in computing project gains? ☐ ☐ ☐

3. Does Finance lead in summing financial gains for executive leadership? ☐ ☐ ☐

4. Does Finance lead in auditing projects 12–24 months later to ensure the gains remain in place? ☐ ☐ ☐

Human Resources

1. Has Lean Six Sigma performance been integrated into performance reviews for leadership, line managers, Champions, and all belts? ☐ ☐ ☐

2. Has Lean Six Sigma performance been integrated into compensation for leadership, line managers, Champions, and all belts? ☐ ☐ ☐

3. Are Lean Six Sigma skills being sought in the recruiting of new employees? ☐ ☐ ☐

1 of 2 **Cont'd.** ━━━▶

Institutionalize the Program Checklist ◄━━━━━━

	Applicable?	Not Completed	Completed

Human Resources (Cont'd.)

4. Has Lean Six Sigma performance been integrated into promotion criteria? ☐ ☐ ☐

5. Is HR a party to managing Lean Six Sigma talent and identifying people for increased responsibilities? ☐ ☐ ☐

Information Technology

1. Is IT involved in Lean Six Sigma software selection and maintenance? ☐ ☐ ☐

2. Does IT manage the software used for project selection, project tracking, and summing the gains? ☐ ☐ ☐

3. Does IT manage the infrastructure for knowledge management? ☐ ☐ ☐

Sales

1. Have Sales personnel been trained in how to communicate Lean Six Sigma to clients? ☐ ☐ ☐

2. Are Sales personnel used to identify customer-focused projects? ☐ ☐ ☐

Operations

1. Has Lean Six Sigma performance been integrated into Operations reviews including corporate, business unit, and plant levels? ☐ ☐ ☐

2. Does Operations feed HR a stream of BBs and GBs identified for training? ☐ ☐ ☐

3. Has GB or BB training been made mandatory for all plant managers and quality managers? ☐ ☐ ☐

Mentor-Mentee and Coaching

1. Have mentoring and coaching needs been identified? ☐ ☐ ☐

2. Have mentor-mentee relationships been established throughout line management? ☐ ☐ ☐

3. Have specific actions and behaviors been identified for all levels of line management? ☐ ☐ ☐

4. Is there a robust method to provide feedback to managers on Lean Six Sigma performance? ☐ ☐ ☐

CHAPTER 13

IMPROVE CONTINUOUSLY

There is an old expression that says, "Eat your own cooking." This is certainly true of Lean Six Sigma, which espouses the need to be proactive and preventive and to focus relentlessly on continuous improvement. If a continuous-improvement program is to have credibility in the eyes of the organization, then the program needs to "practice what it preaches." This **seventh** and final phase of the Deployment Roadmap helps to ensure that the continuous-improvement organization managing Lean Six Sigma does just that—abides by the Lean Six Sigma philosophy of improving continuously. Specific activities in this phase are:

13.01: Improve Continuously ◄━━━━━━━━━━━━━

Improve Continuously

Culture
• Perform periodic culture assessments and act upon findings

Strategy
• Extend the value stream to suppliers and customers

Process
• Review Lean Six Sigma performance
  - Organizationally
  - By business unit
  - By value stream and function
• Grow human capital
• Grow intellectual capital

CULTURE-RELATED ACTIVITIES

Phase 7 has one culture-related activity.

Perform Periodic Culture Assessments and Act Upon Findings

A key part of continuous improvement is continuing the evolution of the culture to one that fully supports continuous-improvement activities. As was discussed in chapter 6, implementation of a program without an accompanying shift in culture will yield limited results. So, in the first phase of the Deployment Roadmap, we began the process of assessing culture and identifying key cultural issues. Additional activities that participants undertake in subsequent phases support the effort of culture change.

At this point in the deployment process, many of the things that support cultural change will already be in place. However, changing culture takes time, and to support continuous improvement it is necessary to sustain the effort and enhance the activities that target culture change.

As part of the continuous-improvement effort, you should periodically assess your organizational culture. The purpose of this ongoing assessment is to determine the direction and rate of change of the various elements of organizational culture and to compare this to the desired ideal culture. Often, the rate of change in the culture varies from location to location and from function to function.

The rate of change in the culture, and the direction of the change, constitute valuable data in terms of not only assessing the impact of targeted activities on culture, but more important, it provides strategic direction for the future. By comparing the results of a cultural assessment to the desired future-state culture, Lean Six Sigma deployment teams can work with leadership to determine additional actions and activities that the organization should undertake to support the desired evolution of the culture. From a process perspective, data are collected and analyzed, as chapter 4 describes.

STRATEGY-RELATED ACTIVITIES

Phase 7 has one strategy-related activity.

Extend the Value Stream to Suppliers and Customers

When initiating a Lean Six Sigma program, an organization typically focuses exclusively on its internal processes. Until the Lean Six Sigma program has been in place for a significant length of time, it is wise to focus on problems and projects that are 100 percent controlled by the organization. In other words, there is no dependency on supplier or customer participation. Anytime the organization requires the support of customers or suppliers to successfully complete a project, it significantly increases the risk of project failure.

The extent of the risk of involving outside parties is a function of how important your organization is to the supplier or customer. If your organization is a significant portion of a supplier's business, the risks are far smaller since the supplier has a large stake in being cooperative. If, on the other hand, your organization is a very small proportion of the supplier's total business, the supplier has little motivation to expend resources to support your project.

Having said this, as the Lean Six Sigma program matures, it is only natural to begin extending the boundaries outward toward customers and suppliers. If you begin to map value streams that include not just your organization, but also supplier and customer organizations, another layer of duplication and waste will quickly become evident.

This waste is more difficult to reduce or eliminate because there are multiple parties involved. However, as the internal continuous-improvement effort matures, a greater proportion of the total waste and variation will come from sources external to your organization. At some point, it will be necessary to extend the continuous-improvement effort to include these other parties in order to produce a sufficient rate of continuous improvement.

PROCESS-RELATED ACTIVITIES

Phase 7 has three process-related activities.

Review Lean Six Sigma Performance at Organizational, Business Unit, and Department and Value Stream Levels

Periodically, the steering committee needs to review the organizational performance of the Lean Six Sigma program as it relates to the program goals. This assessment will answer key questions.

- What is the accrued benefit of the completed projects?
- What has been invested in the program?
- How are the different business units performing relative to goals?
- Have the organization's goals changed, necessitating a change in project selection criteria?
- What corrective actions are required?

We recommend that the steering committee meet quarterly to assess the above points. You should note that as the program matures, this responsibility will move from a steering committee to being embedded in the functions or value streams.

If the program is failing to meet its goals, the steering committee should determine the root causes and take corrective action. If the results are below goal, some inputs to consider are:

- the number of projects started;
- the number of projects successfully completed;
- success ratio (projects completed over projects started) by Champions;
- the total and average gains generated by the projects; and
- the average level of Lean Six Sigma activity for Green Belts and Black Belts.

It is vital to ensure that the team is measuring results, not activity, and that the team implements timely corrective actions. If the goals and objectives developed in the first two phases are results focused, this task is typically straightforward.

Another helpful tool in driving continuous improvement is a "things gone right/things gone wrong analysis" (TGR/TGW). A TGR/TGW analysis is merely a summary, typically bullet points, which the team compiles over the life of the project. The first part of the list is a summary of the positive things that the project team saw or experienced. The second part of the list is a summary of the barriers or inhibiting factors that the team experienced over the life of the project.

Over time, the steering committee compiles and analyzes the TGR/TGW analyses completed over many projects, to identify opportunities for future improvements. The analysis is normally straightforward and in the form of Pareto charts (a rank-ordered bar chart used to categorize—in this case, things gone right and things gone wrong—and prioritize). Most often, you will see clear and consistent patterns in terms of both positive and negative feedback. The Lean Six Sigma steering committee should then use this feedback to minimize or eliminate the most significant barriers to success, as well as to reinforce and increase the frequency of things gone right.

We also recommend a quarterly steering committee report to senior leadership on the performance of the Lean Six Sigma program. This report should focus on how the Lean Six Sigma program aligns with the organization's strategic goals and objectives, as well as its effectiveness in helping the organization achieve those goals. From these quarterly briefings, leadership can determine changes in direction or resourcing.

Grow Human Capital

Part of continuous improvement is upgrading the skills of people involved in carrying out Lean Six Sigma activities. As part of their regular duties, Lean Six Sigma practitioners should evaluate the skills, personalities, and interests of those they are working with to identify high-potential candidates for the Lean Six

Sigma program. Team members who exhibit an affinity for the methodology and have the requisite skills should be targeted as candidates for Green Belt training. Likewise, you should target high-potential Green Belts for Black Belt training and high-level Black Belts, less often, for promotion to Master Black Belt status.

The teams responsible for the Lean Six Sigma program, both on the organizational and the business unit levels, should also monitor the number of active Master Black Belts, Black Belts, and Green Belts within their sphere of operation and have proactive plans in place to replenish those resources as they depart for other responsibilities within the organization. Part of meeting that responsibility is having a list of potential candidates so that as changes in personnel take place, the teams are able to quickly respond and ensure that adequate resources are in place.

Grow Intellectual Capital

Another area that requires continuous-improvement activity is the knowledge management system. For example, over time, improvements can be made in the technology infrastructure that supports knowledge management. These improvements in infrastructure should enhance comprehensive knowledge storage as well as make the knowledge more searchable and usable by others within the organization.

The team can track the volume of information contained within the knowledge management system as well as the number of searches that are undertaken for information in the system. The larger the organization, the more imperative it is that the knowledge management system be continuously improved as the benefits of knowledge management increase in parallel with the increase in the size and complexity of the organization.

Now let's return to the continuous-improvement Maturity Model. The goal of the "Improve Continuously" phase is to continue the migration from an immature continuous-improvement program to one that is fully optimized. Undertaking the activities in the first six phases of the Deployment Roadmap ensures that leadership is addressing the key cultural, strategic, and process issues that enable Lean Six Sigma's success. This final phase focuses on the continuation and enhancement of those activities so that the organization continues to achieve new gains in efficiency and effectiveness.

Go to www.e-mri.net/roadmap.htm to download a free, full-color, 24" x 36" or 11" x 17" PDF of the eMRI Lean Six Sigma Deployment Roadmap.

Improve Continuously Checklist ◀━━━━━━━━━

	Applicable?	Not Completed	Completed

Culture

1. Are periodic cultural assessments performed? ☐ ☐ ☐

2. Do corporate leadership and business unit leadership maintain and modify cultural change activities based on the ongoing assessments? ☐ ☐ ☐

3. Is there an ongoing reward and recognition program for Lean Six Sigma at all levels of the organization? ☐ ☐ ☐

Strategy

1. Are customers and/or suppliers part of the Lean Six Sigma program? ☐ ☐ ☐

2. Are customers and/or suppliers solicited for ideas for Lean Six Sigma projects? ☐ ☐ ☐

3. Are shared savings projects suggested with either customers or suppliers? ☐ ☐ ☐

4. Are customers and/or suppliers invited to participate on Lean Six Sigma teams? ☐ ☐ ☐

5. Are BB resources offered to customers and/or suppliers to assist in problem resolution or do you require they accept your assistance? ☐ ☐ ☐

6. Are Lean Six Sigma training resources offered to customers and/or suppliers or is it required that they receive Lean Six Sigma training? ☐ ☐ ☐

7. Are Lean Six Sigma projects being used for purposes other than cost reduction? ☐ ☐ ☐

Process

1. Is a permanent corporate-level Lean Six Sigma review process in place? ☐ ☐ ☐

2. Is the frequency of corporate reviews established? ☐ ☐ ☐

3. Are the corporate review personnel established? ☐ ☐ ☐

4. Is leadership participating at an appropriate level, and if not, is there a plan to improve participation? ☐ ☐ ☐

1 of 2 **Cont'd.** ━━━━━━▶

Improve Continuously Checklist ◄━━━━━━━━━━

	Applicable?	Not Completed	Completed

Process (Cont'd.)

5. Is a permanent business unit level Lean Six Sigma review process in place? ☐ ☐ ☐

6. Is the frequency of business unit reviews established? ☐ ☐ ☐

7. Is business unit leadership participating at an appropriate level, and if not, is there a plan to improve participation? ☐ ☐ ☐

8. Are Lean Six Sigma assignments viewed as career stepping-stones? ☐ ☐ ☐

9. Is there a Black Belt performance review process in place? ☐ ☐ ☐

10. Is the Black Belt review process integrated into HR systems? ☐ ☐ ☐

11. Is Lean Six Sigma performance integrated into HR systems for line managers? ☐ ☐ ☐

12. Are line management actions and behaviors being monitored, evaluated, and improved? ☐ ☐ ☐

13. Is there an audit system to assess completed projects 12–24 months after closure to ensure gains remain in place? ☐ ☐ ☐

14. Is the knowledge management system being enhanced and improved for content and ease of use? ☐ ☐ ☐

15. Is the queue of potential GBs, BBs, and MBBs growing stronger over time? ☐ ☐ ☐

CHAPTER 14

PITFALLS TO AVOID

Many of the most commonly seen pitfalls in the implementation of Lean Six Sigma are related to shortcutting the deployment process. All too often, organizations—in a rush to realize the benefits of Lean Six Sigma—fail to lay the foundation for sustained success, or they leap into Lean Six Sigma expecting a "free lunch." While it is possible for the organization to shortcut any of the steps in the Lean Six Sigma Deployment Roadmap, we most commonly see the following:

14.01: Common Pitfalls

Cultural Pitfalls	Strategic Pitfalls	Process Pitfalls
• Unassessed culture	• Leadership not aligned	• Jumping into training hoping to save time and money
• Reactive, not proactive, firefighting culture	• Ambiguous goals and objectives	• Projects not properly selected
• Strategically adrift flavor-of-the-month philosophy	• Strategy internally focused, no customer focus	• Projects resource starved
• Not-my-job culture	• Lack of dedicated resources (cutting to success)	• Projects not rigorously tracked
• Resistance to change		• Failure to execute a robust communication plan

CULTURAL PITFALLS

There are five cultural pitfalls.

Unassessed Culture

The most common cultural pitfall is to not consider the issue of culture when implementing a continuous-improvement program. Too often, leadership chooses to pass over the need for cultural change or does not understand how to accomplish it. Each organization's culture is unique. Failure to assess and understand the culture of the organization as it relates to implementing and sustaining a Lean Six Sigma program creates a risk of failure or, at best, increases the time and resources required to realize Lean Six Sigma success. As we discussed in chapter 7, performing a cultural assessment is analogous to turning the lights on in a room full of obstacles. The cultural assessment shows leadership how the organization's culture both supports and inhibits the successful implementation of Lean Six Sigma so that leadership can chart a more effective path to success.

If you do not assess your organization's culture, its structures can lead to the program failing or underperforming in these ways:

- reactive, not proactive, firefighting culture;
- strategically adrift flavor-of-the-month philosophy;
- not-my-job culture; and
- resistance to change.

These pitfalls, for the most part, are cultural characteristics of the organization that do not support Lean Six Sigma and related activities. Virtually all organizational cultures have characteristics that do not support Lean Six Sigma activities. In some cases, there may be many cultural characteristics that do not support Lean Six Sigma. The risk to the Lean Six Sigma program comes not from the presence of the characteristics themselves, but the failure of leadership to understand the culture and to design deployment plans to address the cultural shortcomings as they relate to Lean Six Sigma. It is failing to offset negative cultural aspects, not the presence of the aspects themselves, that creates the risk of failure.

Reactive, Not Proactive, Firefighting Culture

Lean Six Sigma challenges many organizations because they have an established culture of firefighting. Said another way, the organizational culture reacts to crises rather than proactively preventing them. In such organizations, firefighting is considered to be a valuable skill and is rewarded as such. In these cultures, investing resources in proactive, preventive activities is anathema. This is true for two reasons. The first is that firefighting organizations often have no resources to dedicate to preventive activities because there are so many fires to fight. They cannot find a way to break the firefighting cycle and bring resources to bear on preventive activities that would reduce the number of fires. The second reason is that such organizational cultures often prize visible activity and speed. The approach to solving problems in these organizations is "ready, fire, aim." In the context of Lean Six Sigma, such organizations struggle to adhere to the DMAIC methodology; they shortcut the DMAIC methodology to DIC (Define, Improve, Control). They jump from defining the problem to trying to solve the problem. The failure to collect and analyze data (the Measure and Analyze phases of the DMAIC process) normally results in underperforming projects or project failure. After all, if the problem could be solved without data, it probably would have been solved a long time ago.

Strategically Adrift Philosophy

Some leadership teams suffer from what is sometimes called a flavor-of-the-month approach to strategy; that is, the leadership team frequently shifts strategies. Dr. Deming used to state that the organizational leadership had to have "constancy of purpose." In other words, pick a continuous-improvement methodology and stick with it. If leadership is constantly changing the strategic landscape and shifting from program to program, organizational personnel are left adrift. Furthermore, if the organization has been exposed to multiple continuous-improvement programs that were begun as a result of changes in strategic direction or changes in personnel, then the new initiative of Lean Six Sigma will have little credibility.

Not-My-Job Culture

Another cultural barrier that is encountered is the organization-wide mentality that continuous improvement is the job of the quality department. This not-my-job mentality results in a myopic approach to driving continuous improvement within the organization. With few exceptions, such organizations restrict Lean Six Sigma training to the quality function and expect the quality function to generate process improvement without significant support from the rest of the organization. Process functions abdicate responsibility for continuous improvement and the organization places responsibility for failure to improve on the shoulders of the quality function.

Resistance to Change

Resistance to change is a cultural barrier which every organization faces; a large proportion of every organization's population will resist change. The proportion of the organization that resists change and the degree of resistance will vary, based on a host of factors. For example, it is highly likely that a workforce whose average tenure at the company is many years will resist change more than a workforce with an average tenure of just a few years.

STRATEGIC PITFALLS

There are four strategic pitfalls you will need to guard against.

Leadership Not Aligned

If the organizational leadership is not aligned in its vision for continuous improvement, it will not fully support the Lean Six Sigma effort. Lack of support across the entire leadership team will result in islands of support and, thus, islands of excellence. Support by some leaders and not others means it will not be possible to generate improvement across entire value streams. Rather, the organization will achieve ad hoc activity and inconsistent improvement efforts focused on specific functions.

Ambiguous Goals and Objectives

If leadership fails to clearly articulate the goals and objectives for the Lean Six Sigma initiative, it is highly likely that the program will not generate and deliver the desired results. If the organization does not clearly state the goals at the beginning of the program, the planning and execution of the deployment are unlikely to achieve those goals. The result will be errors in resourcing, project selection, and many other areas of the Deployment Roadmap.

Strategy Internally Focused

As I discussed in chapter 6, good project selection requires balancing internal and external focus. All too often, organizations only look inward and focus Lean Six Sigma projects on internal benefits such as cost savings and capacity increases. While such activities are certainly valid, it is imperative that you balance these with long-term improvements in customer satisfaction.

Lack of Dedicated Resources

Organizations get out of Lean Six Sigma what they put into it. Implementing and deploying Lean Six Sigma, creating supporting structures, and supporting project teams cannot be done without a long-term resource commitment. If the organization, upon hitting some financial turbulence, reacts by cutting anything that seems nonessential in the short term, it may undermine or destroy the Lean Six Sigma program. As we saw earlier, Lean Six Sigma is often an important but not urgent activity. As such, it is sometimes undermined by short-term decision making.

Unfortunately, when organizations have knee-jerk reactions to short-term perturbations, they often do long-term damage. In cutting back continuous-improvement activities, management also sends a clear message that continuous improvement is not an essential function.

PROCESS PITFALLS

There are five process pitfalls.

Jumping into Training

Organizations sometimes jump immediately to training Green Belts and Black Belts for several reasons. One is that leadership often fails to realize that training, while necessary, is not sufficient for success. In other words, no thought has been given to the other support processes the Lean Six Sigma Deployment Roadmap identifies. At other times, leadership is eager to begin Lean Six Sigma projects and generate results, with the idea of putting the supporting infrastructure in place later. Unfortunately, postponing the necessary steps until later often means that the initial waves of project teams do not have the necessary support or, even worse, the supporting infrastructure is never put in place, jeopardizing program success.

Projects Not Properly Selected

It is essential to select the right projects to deliver maximum value to the organization while concurrently minimizing the risk of project failure. If the project selection process is suboptimal, the program suffers. Poor project selection can be the result of several phenomena. First, if the Champions, who are responsible for project selection, are not trained properly, they will likely select suboptimal projects. Another cause of poor project selection sometimes is that leadership fails to clearly communicate the key goals and objectives that, in essence, constitute the project selection criteria. That is, leadership clearly understands the goals and objectives, but does not clearly articulate them to others. Finally, leaders sometimes fail to update the organization's key goals and objectives over time. Goals and objectives change as the organization and its competitive environment evolve. A failure to update the project selection criteria as this evolution takes place results in suboptimal project selection.

Projects Resource Starved

All too often, organizations expect people with functional responsibilities to magically add Green Belt or Black Belt responsibilities to an already full plate and generate Lean Six Sigma project success. Unless the organizational leadership and the project Champions ensure that Black Belts and Green Belts are given sufficient time to lead projects, there is a high probability of project failure. Ideally, Black Belts and Green Belts dedicate 100 percent of their time to their Lean Six Sigma projects. This may be unrealistic in some organizations. However, a Green Belt's or Black Belt's minimum commitment to leading a project is 25 percent. Anything less significantly increases the risk of project failure.

Projects Not Rigorously Tracked

Failure to have a robust system in place to track projects substantially increases the risk of projects falling behind schedule or failing to meet their goals and objectives. It is imperative that there be a series of reviews and/or tollgates as the team proceeds through the project. In this fashion, issues impeding project success will be identified quickly so that remedial action can be taken and the project is put back on track.

Failure to Execute a Robust Communication Plan

There are myriad constituent groups that Lean Six Sigma programs affect, and it is important that proactive communication takes place among these groups. Perhaps most important is the internal communication with the leadership and functional managers to create pull for the Lean Six Sigma program. You want to have a structured communication effort that ensures that leaders and managers understand the benefit of Lean Six Sigma and how it can help them achieve their business goals and objectives. If leaders and managers understand how the use of Lean Six Sigma will allow them to move their part of the organization forward, it will create pull for Lean Six Sigma activity.

The other failure we often see is the failure to communicate with the workforce as a whole about Lean Six Sigma. Unfortunately, leadership often believes that the communication system is robust and all employees are fully aware of the Lean Six Sigma program, its benefits, and its activities. Communication and information to lower-level associates is often far less than management believes. If part of the goal of the Lean Six Sigma program is to begin involving the organizational culture, then it is imperative that this type of communication be extremely robust.

CHAPTER 15

CONCLUSION

In today's increasingly competitive environment, Lean Six Sigma offers organizational leadership a way to increase value and improve profitability through the delivery of higher levels of productivity, quality, and customer satisfaction. Once leadership conveys what is important, we eliminate non-value-added activity and time (waste) associated with the important processes, and then get the remaining value-added steps on target with minimum variation. Regardless of the type of organization—public, private, nonprofit, governmental, small, or large—Lean Six Sigma is a proven methodology that can yield significant improvements in performance.

The key to success in implementing and sustaining Lean Six Sigma is to build a firm foundation for project activities by following the Lean Six Sigma roadmap. The Lean Six Sigma Deployment Roadmap provides leadership with a clear set of required steps and activities to ensure that the program delivers maximum benefit to the organization. It ensures that the organization undertakes the necessary actions and sets up the necessary infrastructure to optimize Lean Six Sigma success. It does this not only by addressing process issues and infrastructure, but also by addressing the issues of organizational culture and strategy.

If you follow it, the roadmap will ensure not only that your Lean Six Sigma program will be successful but that, over time, it will become part of your organization's way of doing business. That is, process improvement, and the improvement in financial results that follow, will be everyday occurrences that provide the organization with a long-term competitive advantage.

GLOSSARY

Analyze – The third phase of the Lean Six Sigma DMAIC methodology. The primary activity in this phase is the analysis of data collected in the Measure phase. In this phase, many of the statistical tools that Lean Six Sigma is known for, such as statistical process control, hypothesis testing, correlation, and regression, are used.

Black Belt – A person who leads Lean Six Sigma project teams and has received four weeks of training in the Lean Six Sigma methodology in preparation for doing so.

Champions – Members of an organization's management who are responsible for selecting projects, providing resources, and removing barriers for Lean Six Sigma teams. Champions, by virtue of their responsibilities, need to have positions relatively high in the organization.

communication plan – A formal plan that delineates the constituent groups that will be given information about the Lean Six Sigma program, and defines the content of that information and the delivery mechanism, as well as the frequency of dissemination.

continuous improvement – The endless cycle whereby a process is observed or measured and the observations and measurements used to improve process performance. Dr. Deming referred to the cycle as the Plan, Do, Check, Act cycle.

Control – The fifth and last phase of the Lean Six Sigma DMAIC methodology. Activities in this phase center on ensuring that the improvements made in the Improve phase are made permanent so that the business process does not revert back to its prior state.

correlation – A statistical test that indicates the strength of relationship between two variables. In Lean Six Sigma, it is most often used to determine how strong an influence a process input has on a process output.

cultural assessment – The completed analysis of the answers to a series of questions given to a sample of the organization for purposes of assessing organizational culture. The assessment is used to identify cultural factors that support or inhibit the implementation of Lean Six Sigma.

culture – The pervasive beliefs, behaviors, and ways of doing things in an organization. Organizational culture may vary from department to department and location to location.

defect – Anything that causes a service or product to be nonconforming relative to customer requirements. Defects are also commonly known as errors or mistakes.

Define – The first phase of the Lean Six Sigma project methodology in which the primary activities are scoping the project, defining the team composition, and creating process maps.

Deming, Dr. W. Edwards – A renowned continuous-improvement expert who is best known for his work in Japan from 1950 to 1980. Deming was a strong proponent of variation reduction.

deployment teams – They exist at the organizational and/ or business unit level. They are tasked with the initial implementation of the Lean Six Sigma program.

designed experiments – A method of statistically analyzing a process through controlled manipulation of the process inputs. The result of designed experimentation is a mathematical model of the process that allows process optimization.

DMAIC – An acronym for the Lean Six Sigma project methodology of Define, Measure, Analyze, Improve, and Control. Every Lean Six Sigma project follows the DMAIC methodology.

excessive processing – Work or activity that the customer is unwilling to pay for.

firefighting – Running from crisis to crisis, most often putting in place quick fixes to lessen or mitigate the crisis, but not putting in place long-term solutions to prevent recurrence.

flow – The movement of materials and information through a value stream. Optimally, the flow is continuous.

Green Belt – A person who leads Lean Six Sigma project teams or supports Black Belts leading the project teams, who has received two weeks of training in Lean Six Sigma methodology in preparation for doing so.

hypothesis testing – A test that is used to determine which of two mutually exclusive hypotheses should be concluded to be true. For example, one specific test can be used to determine whether one should conclude if a process in one location has less variation (or not) than a comparable process in a second location.

Improve – The fourth phase in the Lean Six Sigma DMAIC methodology. Predominant in this phase is the use of Lean tools and techniques to generate process improvement.

inventory – Most typical is manufacturing work product in the form of raw material, work in progress (WIP), or finished product. It also can exist in the service environment, for example, in the form of paperwork or e-mail in an inbox.

knowledge management – The practice of identifying, collecting, storing, and disseminating knowledge.

Lean – A methodical approach to shortening the time between the customer's order and the delivery of the product by eliminating waste and maximizing flow.

Lean Six Sigma – A continuous-improvement methodology that merges the strengths of Lean with the strengths of Six Sigma. It uses the rigor of the DMAIC methodology Six Sigma is known for, and integrates the philosophy, tools, and techniques of Lean Operations.

Lean Six Sigma Deployment Roadmap – A seven-phase process that identifies the specific processes, systems, and activities that need to take place, and the sequence in which they need to take place, so that the organization can apply resources optimally to derive maximum benefit from the Lean Six Sigma program.

Master Black Belt – A person who has exhibited such mastery of Lean Six Sigma methodology that he or she is elevated to a position known as a Master Black Belt. Master Black Belts serve as coaches and mentors to Black Belts and Green Belts, conduct Green Belt and Black Belt training, and often serve as the strategic interface between the organization's leadership and Lean Six Sigma program activities.

Maturity Model – A model that categorizes continuous-improvement programs into five levels: Initial, Managed, Defined, Leading, and Optimizing. At each level, the inputs appropriate for a program at that level are shown, as well as the outputs for that level of the program.

Measure – The second phase of the Lean Six Sigma DMAIC methodology. The primary activities in this phase are determining what data and measurements need to be collected, creating measurement plans, assessing measurement systems, and collecting data.

measurement system assessment – The determination of whether a measurement system is trustworthy via the use of data and statistical tools and methods.

motion – The movement of people or machines in the performance of their work.

non-value-added – Any activity or work performed that the customer is not willing to pay for.

overproduction – Producing more product or service than the customer requires. Overproduction results in additional forms of waste such as inventory and an increase in defects produced.

process control – An activity cycle in which data is collected from the process, the data is analyzed using tools such as statistical process control, and the analysis is used to drive improvements in the process inputs. It is a proactive, preventive philosophy for continuous improvement.

process mapping – The act of creating a visual representation of a process. Types of process maps include flowcharts, SIPOC maps, swim lanes, and value-stream maps. These maps are then utilized as part of driving process improvement.

process thinking – Conceptually understanding that the key to continuous improvement is to focus on the process. Any improvements made to the process will manifest themselves as improvements in product and service quality. In other words, product follows process.

product control – A cycle in which the output from the process (the product) is inspected and any nonconforming product is removed prior to delivery to the customer. Product control is, in essence, a filtering mechanism that screens out a nonconforming product before the customer receives it. Product control does not lead to continuous improvement.

product thinking – The belief that quality can be inspected into the product or service. This means that 100 percent of the product or service is inspected after it is produced, but before it is given to the customer. Any defects or errors are then corrected before the product or service is given to the customer. Product thinking can lead to 100 percent of the product or service the customer receives as meeting their requirements. However, the costs of inspection and rework have a devastating effect on productivity.

productivity – The ratio of output produced to inputs used. The greater the quantity of output produced and the fewer inputs required, the higher the productivity.

project charter – A succinct document used to describe and scope a Lean Six Sigma project.

project scope – Defines the size and boundaries of a specific Lean Six Sigma project. It describes what is included in the project and what is excluded.

pull system – A system whereby each step in the process produces only what the customer needs, when the customer needs it. Primarily, pull systems reduce overproduction and inventory.

push system – A system whereby each step in the process continues to produce product or service even if the customer does not require any. Push systems result in an inventory between each step of the process.

quality – Defined in Lean Six Sigma as on target with minimum variation. That is, the process should be centered on the customer's target, with minimum variation around the target. This is in opposition to the product definition of quality, which is meeting the customer's requirements (the specifications).

regression – A statistical technique most commonly used to develop a mathematical model of a process. The model is an equation that describes the output of the process in terms of the statistically significant inputs.

SIPOC – A five-column process map with the column headers of supplier, input, process step, output, and customer, respectively. The first letters of the column headers create the acronym SIPOC. It is often used in Lean Six Sigma to create a visual representation of a process.

Six Sigma – A continuous-improvement methodology that focuses on minimizing variation around the target value. Six Sigma projects all use the DMAIC methodology and often involve significant use of data and statistical tools and methods for analyzing data.

specifications – Also known as customer requirements, specifications are the upper and lower bounds of what the customer will accept.

statistical process control – A technique used to determine whether a process is statistically in control (the process is consistent over time), or out of control (the process is inconsistent or changing over time).

steering committee – The team that monitors ongoing activities of the Lean Six Sigma program and drives its continuous improvement. The steering committee typically takes over from the deployment team in phase 6 ("Institutionalize the Program") of the Lean Six Sigma Deployment Roadmap.

strategy – A plan, method, or series of maneuvers for obtaining a specific business goal or result.

target value – What the customer considers a perfect product or service.

team members – Process experts that support the Green Belt or Black Belt leading a Lean Six Sigma project team.

transportation – The movement of material, parts, or finished goods between processes or locations. For example, moving product into and out of storage areas or moving a truckload of product to another location.

value-added – Any work or activity that both changes the form, fit, or function, and the customer is willing to pay for it. It must do both to be value-added.

value stream – The entire set of steps and activities required to produce product or service for the customer. A value stream cuts across functional boundaries and involves many of the organization's departments and work areas. Value streams can extend outside the organization, toward suppliers and customers, if appropriate.

voice of the customer (VOC) – A set of customer wants and needs prioritized by importance. VOC is used to improve the design and quality of the products and services offered to the customer. The voice of the customer can be obtained through myriad sources such as surveys, interviews, and focus groups.

waiting – Idle time of people, material, or equipment between operations or events.

waste – Anything that is non-value-added. Forms of waste are defects, overproduction, waiting, unused resources, transportation, inventory, excessive motion, and excessive processing.

White Belt or Yellow Belt – Someone who has been trained to an awareness level in the Lean Six Sigma methodology, but is not capable of leading Lean Six Sigma teams. White and Yellow Belts typically receive between one-half to two days of training in Lean Six Sigma.

INDEX

G

H

I

reporting software, choosing, 132
resource requirements, program, 81–82, 183
resources, insufficient, 46–47
reward and recognition programs, creating, 117–119, 127
reworked, definition of, 22
risk criteria, 107

S

scope of program, determining, 77
scoring systems, project selection, 108
scrapped, definition of, 22
7 Habits of Highly Effective People, The (Covey), 48
Seven-Phase Lean Six Sigma Deployment Roadmap, 64–65, 63 fig. 6.04
sigma levels, indices, 30, 31 fig. 2.07
Six Sigma
    goal of, 9
    Lean merged with, 16–17
skills, hard/soft, 142
SMARTEN Program, 88
soft skills, 142
software, choosing program, 130–132
sponsors, project. *see* Champions
steering committees, role of, 35, 80, 172–173
strategic pitfalls, 179 fig. 14.01, 182–183
strategy
    for deployment plans, 90–93
    element of, 59–61, 60 fig. 6.01, 61 fig. 6.02
    establishing project-related processes, 100–103
    internally focused, 183
    Lean Six Sigma, 31, 31 fig. 2.08
strategy-related activities
    create deployment plans, 90–93
    create joint integration plans, 162–163
    create supporting infrastructure, 126–128
    engage leaders, 71–82
    establish project-related processes, 100–103
    identify and deploy resources, 137–146, 137 fig. 11.01
    improve continuously, 171
success
    establishing metrics for, 92–93
    records of, 56–57
suggestions, project, 108
suppliers, communication with, 130

T

U

V

W

ABOUT THE AUTHOR

Keith Gardner is president of eMRI, a consulting and training firm specializing in Lean Six Sigma and process improvement. For the past 16 years, he has specialized in assisting organizations with the implementation of Lean Six Sigma programs. This has included working with executive leadership on strategic and cultural issues, as well as coordinating and leading the training and mentoring of Green Belts, Black Belts, and Master Black Belts.

Prior to entering the consulting business, Keith held a series of positions in manufacturing, continuous improvement, and engineering. Most recently, prior to joining eMRI, he was director of engineering for a firm serving Fortune 500 clients.

Keith received his MBA from the University of Michigan where he graduated with high distinction. He also holds a bachelor of science degree in chemical engineering from Carnegie Mellon University.

He may be reached at kgardner@e-mri.net.